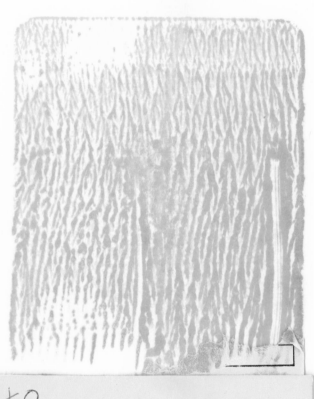

+O

PRINTED IN U.S.A.

# The Laplace Transform:
# An Introduction

by **Earl D. Rainville**

*Professor of Mathematics*
*The University of Michigan*

The Macmillan Company, New York
Collier-Macmillan Limited, London

Library of Congress catalog card number: 62-19754

The Macmillan Company, New York
Collier-Macmillan Canada, Ltd., Toronto, Ontario

*Printed in the United States of America*

Some material included in this book is from Rainville: *Elementary Differential Equations,* Second Edition, ©1958 by The Macmillan Company, and Rainville: *A Short Course in Differential Equations,* Second Edition, ©1958 by The Macmillan Company.

# Preface

I have tried to present here a treatment of the Laplace transform which can be read by a student who has had a course in calculus and at least a few weeks of differential equations.

This book can be used as a supplementary text in elementary differential equations, or in any other intermediate level course in which a brief study of the Laplace transform is desired. There is at least enough material here for a short course at ordinary speed.

It is my hope that the book will prove useful for self study for people who need some knowledge of transform methods but who do not have time available for a longer study.

In writing any text the author must choose a technique of exposition which may lie between two extremes, the presentation of a large amount of material in compact form and the elaborate explanation of a much smaller number of topics. My writing leans toward the latter extreme because I write books to explain the subjects to students, not to their instructors, and in my teaching I have more than once encountered a student who was not a mathematical genius.

In the first, second, and fifth chapters I have tried to present that part of the Laplace transform theory and technique which is more elementary than the complex inversion integral. The remaining chapters are devoted to applications, with much attention given to the question of when the transform method is a desirable one to use.

By means of detailed explanations and careful selection of topics, I have attempted to foster in the reader sufficient skill to permit him to solve by himself many problems which are allotted space in a longer book. There are more than two hundred exercises for the student and they contain both drill problems and substantial additions to the material in the text.

I cannot help but be affected by the fact that for many years I have taught from R. V. Churchill's books on the Laplace transform. I did, as usual, refrain from consulting other books on the subject while writing my own.

The student who wishes to acquire more material on the Laplace transform than is available in this short book might well turn next to R. V. Churchill, *Operational Mathematics*, 2nd ed., New York, McGraw-Hill Book Co., 1958.

EARL D. RAINVILLE

# Table of contents

## Chapter 6.  *Partial Differential Equations*

# Elementary Properties

## 1. *The Transform Concept*

The reader is already familiar with some operators which transform functions into functions. An outstanding example is the differential operator $D$ which transforms each function of a large class (those possessing a derivative) into another function. In this book we study another transformation (a mapping of functions onto functions) which has played an important role in both pure and applied mathematics in the past few decades.

The operator $L$, to be introduced in §2, is particularly effective in the study of boundary value problems involving linear differential equations with constant coefficients.

One class of transformations, which are called integral transforms, may be defined by

$$(1) \qquad T\{F(t)\} = \int_{-\infty}^{\infty} K(s, t) \, F(t) \, dt = f(s).$$

Given a function $K(s, t)$, called the kernel of the transformation, equation (1) associates with each $F(t)$, of the class of functions for which the above integral exists, a function $f(s)$ defined by (1). Generalizations and abstractions of (1), as well as studies of special cases, are to be found in profusion in mathematical literature.

Various particular choices of $K(s, t)$ in (1) have led to special transforms each with its own properties to make it useful in specific circumstances. The transform defined by choosing

$$K(s, t) = 0, \quad \text{for } t < 0,$$
$$= e^{-st}, \quad \text{for } t \geqq 0,$$

is the one to which this book is devoted.

# 2. Definition of the Laplace Transform

Let $F(t)$ be any function such that the integrations encountered may be legitimately performed on $F(t)$. The *Laplace transform* of $F(t)$ is denoted by $L\{F(t)\}$ and is defined by

$$(1) \qquad L\{F(t)\} = \int_0^\infty e^{-st}F(t)\ dt.$$

The integral in (1) is a function of the parameter $s$; call that function $f(s)$. We may write

$$(2) \qquad L\{F(t)\} = \int_0^\infty e^{-st}F(t)\ dt = f(s).$$

It is customary to refer to $f(s)$, as well as to the symbol $L\{F(t)\}$, as the transform, or the Laplace transform, of $F(t)$.

We may also look upon (2) as a definition of a Laplace operator $L$ which transforms each function $F(t)$, of a certain set of functions, into some function $f(s)$.

It is easy to show that if the integral in (2) does converge, it will do so for all $s$ greater than* some fixed value $s_0$. That is, equation (2) will define $f(s)$ for $s > s_0$. In extreme cases the integral may converge for all finite $s$.

It is important that the operator $L$, like the differential operator $D$, is a linear operator. If $F_1(t)$ and $F_2(t)$ have Laplace transforms and if $c_1$ and $c_2$ are any constants,

$$(3) \qquad L\{c_1F_1(t) + c_2F_2(t)\} = c_1L\{F_1(t)\} + c_2L\{F_2(t)\}.$$

Using elementary properties of definite integrals, the student can easily show the validity of equation (3).

We shall hereafter employ the relation (3) without restating the fact that the operator $L$ is a linear one.

# 3. Transforms of Elementary Functions

The transforms of certain exponential and trigonometric functions and of polynomials will now be obtained. These results enter our work frequently throughout the remainder of the book.

*Example (a).* Find $L\{e^{kt}\}$.

We proceed as follows:

$$L\{e^{kt}\} = \int_0^\infty e^{-st} \cdot e^{kt}\ dt = \int_0^\infty e^{-(s-k)t}\ dt.$$

For $s \leqq k$, the exponent on $e$ is positive or zero and the integral diverges. For $s > k$, the integral converges.

---

*If $s$ is not to be restricted to real values, the convergence takes place for all $s$ with real part greater than some fixed value.

Therefore, for $s > k$,

$$L\{e^{kt}\} = \int_0^\infty e^{-(s-k)t}\, dt = \left[\frac{-e^{-(s-k)t}}{s-k}\right]_0^\infty = 0 + \frac{1}{s-k}.$$

Thus we find that

(1)
$$L\{e^{kt}\} = \frac{1}{s-k}, \qquad s > k.$$

Note the special case $k = 0$:

(2)
$$L\{1\} = \frac{1}{s}, \qquad s > 0.$$

*Example (b).*   Obtain $L\{\sin kt\}$.

From any elementary calculus*, or by employing integration by parts twice, we obtain

$$\int e^{ax} \sin mx\, dx = \frac{e^{ax}(a \sin mx - m \cos mx)}{a^2 + m^2} + C.$$

Since

$$L\{\sin kt\} = \int_0^\infty e^{-st} \sin kt\, dt,$$

it follows that

(3)
$$L\{\sin kt\} = \left[\frac{e^{-st}(-s \sin kt - k \cos kt)}{s^2 + k^2}\right]_0^\infty.$$

For positive $s$, $e^{-st} \to 0$ as $t \to \infty$.   Furthermore, $\sin kt$ and $\cos kt$ are bounded as $t \to \infty$.   Therefore (3) yields

$$L\{\sin kt\} = 0 - \frac{1(0 - k)}{s^2 + k^2},$$

or

(4)
$$L\{\sin kt\} = \frac{k}{s^2 + k^2}, \qquad s > 0.$$

The result

(5)
$$L\{\cos kt\} = \frac{s}{s^2 + k^2}, \qquad s > 0,$$

can be obtained in a similar manner from the elementary formula

(6)
$$\int e^{ax} \cos mx\, dx = \frac{e^{ax}(a \cos mx + m \sin mx)}{a^2 + m^2} + C.$$

*For example, E. D. Rainville, *Unified Calculus and Analytic Geometry*, New York, Macmillan, 1961, p. 345.

*Example (c).* Obtain $L\{t^n\}$ for $n$ a positive integer.
By definition

$$L\{t^n\} = \int_0^\infty e^{-st}t^n\, dt.$$

Let us attack the integral by integration by parts with the choice exhibited in the table.

| $t^n$ | $e^{-st}\, dt$ |
| --- | --- |
| $nt^{n-1}\, dt$ | $-\dfrac{1}{s}e^{-st}$ |

We thus obtain

(7) $$\int_0^\infty e^{-st}t^n\, dt = \left[\frac{-t^n e^{-st}}{s}\right]_0^\infty + \frac{n}{s}\int_0^\infty e^{-st}t^{n-1}\, dt.$$

For $s > 0$ and $n > 0$, the first term on the right in (7) is zero and we are left with

$$\int_0^\infty e^{-st}t^n\, dt = \frac{n}{s}\int_0^\infty e^{-st}t^{n-1}\, dt, \qquad s > 0,$$

or

(8) $$L\{t^n\} = \frac{n}{s}L\{t^{n-1}\}, \qquad s > 0.$$

From (8) we may conclude that, for $n > 1$,

$$L\{t^{n-1}\} = \frac{n-1}{s}L\{t^{n-2}\}$$

so that

(9) $$L\{t^n\} = \frac{n(n-1)}{s^2}L\{t^{n-2}\}.$$

Iteration of this process yields

$$L\{t^n\} = \frac{n(n-1)(n-2)\cdots 2\cdot 1}{s^n}L\{t^0\}.$$

By Example (a) above we have $L\{t^0\} = L\{1\} = s^{-1}$. Hence, for $n$ a positive integer,

(10) $$L\{t^n\} = \frac{n!}{s^{n+1}}, \qquad s > 0.$$

The Laplace transform of $F(t)$ will exist even if the object function $F(t)$ is discontinuous, provided the integral in the definition of $L\{F(t)\}$ exists. Little will be done at this time with specific discontinuous $F(t)$ because more efficient methods for obtaining such transforms are to be developed later in the book.

*Example (d).*   Find the Laplace transform of $H(t)$ where

$$H(t) = t, \quad 0 < t < 4,$$
$$= 5, \quad t > 4.$$

Note that the fact that $H(t)$ is not defined at $t = 0$ and $t = 4$ has no bearing whatever on the existence, or the value, of $L\{H(t)\}$. We turn to the definition of $L\{H(t)\}$ to obtain

$$L\{H(t)\} = \int_0^\infty e^{-st} H(t) \, dt$$

$$= \int_0^4 e^{-st} t \, dt + \int_4^\infty e^{-st} 5 \, dt.$$

Using integration by parts on the next to last integral above, we soon arrive, for $s > 0$, at

$$L\{H(t)\} = \left[ -\frac{t}{s} e^{-st} - \frac{1}{s^2} e^{-st} \right]_0^4 + \left[ -\frac{5}{s} e^{-st} \right]_4^\infty$$

$$= -\frac{4e^{-4s}}{s} - \frac{e^{-4s}}{s^2} + 0 + \frac{1}{s^2} - 0 + \frac{5e^{-4s}}{s}$$

$$= \frac{1}{s^2} + \frac{e^{-4s}}{s} - \frac{e^{-4s}}{s^2}.$$

## EXERCISES

**1.** By using equation (6) above, show that

$$L\{\cos kt\} = \frac{s}{s^2 + k^2}, \, s > 0.$$

**2.** Obtain $L\{t^2 - 3t + 5\}$.    *Ans.* $\dfrac{2}{s^3} - \dfrac{3}{s^2} + \dfrac{5}{s}, \quad s > 0.$

**3.** Obtain $L\{\frac{1}{2}t^3 + t^2 - 1\}$.    *Ans.* $\dfrac{3}{s^4} + \dfrac{2}{s^3} - \dfrac{1}{s}, \quad s > 0.$

**4.** Evaluate $L\{e^{-4t} + 3e^{-2t}\}$.    *Ans.* $\dfrac{2(2s + 7)}{(s + 2)(s + 4)}, \quad s > -2.$

**5.** Evaluate $L\{2e^{3t} - e^{-3t}\}$.    *Ans.* $\dfrac{s + 9}{s^2 - 9}, \quad s > 3.$

**6.** Show that $L\{\cosh kt\} = \dfrac{s}{s^2 - k^2}, \quad s > |k|.$

**7.** Show that $L\{\sinh kt\} = \dfrac{k}{s^2 - k^2}, \quad s > |k|.$

**8.** Use the trigonometric identity $\cos^2 A = \frac{1}{2}(1 + \cos 2A)$ and equation (5), §3, to evaluate $L\{\cos^2 kt\}$.

*Ans.* $\dfrac{s^2 + 2k^2}{s(s^2 + 4k^2)}, \quad s > 0.$

**9.** Parallel the method suggested in Ex. 8 to obtain $L\{\sin^2 kt\}$.

$$Ans. \ \frac{2k^2}{s(s^2 + 4k^2)}, \quad s > 0.$$

**10.** Obtain $L\{\sin^2 kt\}$ directly from the answer to Ex. 8.

**11.** Evaluate $L\{\sin kt \cos kt\}$ with the aid of a trigonometric identity.

$$Ans. \ \frac{k}{s^2 + 4k^2}, \quad s > 0.$$

**12.** Evaluate $L\{e^{-at} - e^{-bt}\}$.      $Ans. \ \dfrac{b - a}{(s + a)(s + b)}, \quad s > \mathrm{Max}(-a, -b).$

**13.** Find $L\{\psi(t)\}$ where

$$\psi(t) = 4, \quad 0 < t < 1,$$
$$= 3, \quad t > 1.$$

$$Ans. \ \frac{1}{s}(4 - e^{-s}), \quad s > 0.$$

**14.** Find $L\{\varphi(t)\}$ where

$$\varphi(t) = 1, \quad 0 < t < 2,$$
$$= t, \quad t > 2.$$

$$Ans. \ \frac{1}{s} + \frac{e^{-2s}}{s} + \frac{e^{-2s}}{s^2}, \quad s > 0.$$

**15.** Find $L\{A(t)\}$ where

$$A(t) = 0, \quad 0 < t < 1,$$
$$= t, \quad 1 < t < 2,$$
$$= 0, \quad t > 2.$$

$$Ans. \ \left(\frac{1}{s^2} + \frac{1}{s}\right)e^{-s} - \left(\frac{1}{s^2} + \frac{2}{s}\right)e^{-2s}, \quad s > 0.$$

**16.** Find $L\{B(t)\}$ where

$$B(t) = \sin 2t, \quad 0 < t < \pi,$$
$$= 0, \quad t > \pi.$$

$$Ans. \ \frac{2(1 - e^{-\pi s})}{s^2 + 4}, \quad s > 0.$$

## 4. *Sectionally Continuous Functions*

It soon becomes tiresome to test each $F(t)$ we encounter to determine whether the integral

$$(1) \qquad \int_0^\infty e^{-st}F(t)\ dt$$

exists for some range of values of $s$. We therefore seek a fairly large class of functions for which we can prove once and for all that the integral (1) exists.

One of our avowed interests in the Laplace transform is in its usefulness as a tool in solving problems in more or less elementary applications, particularly boundary value problems in differential equations. Therefore we do not hesitate to restrict our study to functions $F(t)$ which are continuous or even differentiable, except possibly at a discrete set of points, in the semi-infinite range $t \geq 0$.

For such functions, the existence of the integral (1) can be endangered only at points of discontinuity of $F(t)$ or by divergence due to behavior of the integrand as $t \to \infty$.

In elementary calculus we found that finite discontinuities, or finite jumps, of the integrand did not interfere with the existence of the integral. We therefore introduce a term to describe functions which are continuous except for such jumps.

DEFINITION: The function $F(t)$ is said to be *sectionally continuous* over the closed interval $a \leq t \leq b$ if that interval can be divided into a finite number of subintervals $c \leq t \leq d$ such that in each subinterval:

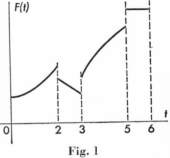

1. $F(t)$ is continuous in the open interval $c < t < d$,

2. $F(t)$ approaches a limit as $t$ approaches each endpoint from within the interval; that is, $\underset{t \to c^+}{\text{Lim }} F(t)$ and $\underset{t \to d^-}{\text{Lim }} F(t)$ exist.

Figure 1 shows an $F(t)$ which is sectionally continuous over the interval $0 \leq t \leq 6$.

The student should realize that there is

Fig. 1

no implication that $F(t)$ must be sectionally continuous for $L\{F(t)\}$ to exist. Indeed, we shall meet several counter-examples to any such notion. The concept of sectionally continuous functions will, in §6, play a role in a set of sufficient conditions for the existence of the transform.

## 5. *Functions of Exponential Order*

If the integral of $e^{-st}F(t)$ between the limits 0 and $t_0$ exists for every finite positive $t_0$, the only remaining threat to the existence of the transform

$$(1) \qquad \int_0^\infty e^{-st}F(t)\, dt$$

is the behavior of the integrand as $t \to \infty$.

We know that

$$(2) \qquad \int_0^\infty e^{-ct}\, dt$$

converges for $c > 0$. This arouses our interest in functions $F(t)$ which, for large $t (t \geq t_0)$, are essentially bounded by some exponential $e^{bt}$ so that the integrand in (1) will behave like the integrand in (2) for $s$ large enough.

DEFINITION: The function $F(t)$ is said to be of *exponential order as* $t \to \infty$ if there exist constants $M$ and $b$ and a fixed $t$-value $t_0$ such that

$$(3) \qquad\qquad |F(t)| < Me^{bt}, \qquad \text{for } t \geqq t_0.$$

If $b$ is to be emphasized, we say that $F(t)$ is of the order of $e^{bt}$ as $t \to \infty$. We also write

$$(4) \qquad\qquad F(t) = O(e^{bt}), \qquad t \to \infty,$$

to mean that $F(t)$ is of exponential order, the exponential being $e^{bt}$, as $t \to \infty$. That is, (4) is another way of expressing (3).

Exponential functions enter our work frequently. Whenever the exponent on $e$ is at all complicated we shall use a common notation

$$(5) \qquad\qquad \exp(u) = e^u$$

for convenience in printing. The functional form $\exp(u)$ is employed, for example, in equation (7) below and in Example (b), page 9.

The integral in (1) may be split into parts as follows:

$$(6) \qquad \int_0^\infty e^{-st}F(t)\,dt = \int_0^{t_0} e^{-st}F(t)\,dt + \int_{t_0}^\infty e^{-st}F(t)\,dt.$$

If $F(t)$ is of exponential order, $F(t) = O(e^{bt})$, the last integral in equation (6) exists because from the inequality (3) it follows that, for $s > b$,

$$(7) \qquad \int_{t_0}^\infty |e^{-st}F(t)|\,dt < M\int_{t_0}^\infty e^{-st} \cdot e^{bt}\,dt = \frac{M \exp\,[-t_0(s-b)]}{s-b}.$$

For $s > b$, the last member of (7) approaches zero as $t_0 \to \infty$. Therefore the last integral in (6) is absolutely convergent* for $s > b$. We have proved the following result.

THEOREM 1. *If the integral of $e^{-st}F(t)$ between the limits 0 and $t_0$ exists for every finite positive $t_0$ and if $F(t)$ is of exponential order, $F(t) = O(e^{bt})$, as $t \to \infty$, the Laplace transform*

$$L\{F(t)\} = \int_0^\infty e^{-st}F(t)\,dt = f(s)$$

*exists for $s > b$.*

We know that a function which is sectionally continuous over an interval is integrable over that interval. This leads us to the following useful special case of Theorem 1.

THEOREM 2. *If $F(t)$ is sectionally continuous over every finite interval in the range $t \geqq 0$, and if $F(t)$ is of exponential order, $F(t) = O(e^{bt})$ as $t \to \infty$, the Laplace transform $L\{F(t)\}$ exists for $s > b$.*

---

*If complex $s$ is to be used, the integral converges for $\mathrm{Re}(s) > b$.

Functions of exponential order play a dominant role throughout our work. It is therefore wise to develop proficiency in determining whether or not a specified function is of exponential order.

Surely if a constant $b$ exists such that

(8) $$\operatorname{Lim}_{t \to \infty} \left[ e^{-bt} |F(t)| \right]$$

exists, the function $F(t)$ is of exponential order, indeed of the order of $e^{bt}$. To see this, let the value of the limit (8) be $K \neq 0$. Then, for $t$ large enough, $|e^{-bt}F(t)|$ can be made as close to $K$ as is desired, so certainly

$$|e^{-bt}F(t)| < 2K.$$

Therefore, for $t$ sufficiently large,

(9) $$|F(t)| < Me^{bt},$$

with $M = 2K$. If the limit in (8) is zero, we may write (9) with $M = 1$.

On the other hand, if for every fixed $c$,

(10) $$\operatorname{Lim}_{t \to \infty} \left[ e^{-ct} |F(t)| \right] = \infty,$$

the function $F(t)$ is not of exponential order. For, assume $b$ exists such that

(11) $$|F(t)| < Me^{bt}, \qquad t \geqq t_0.$$

Then the choice $c = 2b$ would yield, by (11),

$$|e^{-2bt}F(t)| < Me^{-bt}$$

so that $e^{-2bt}F(t) \to 0$ as $t \to \infty$ which disagrees with (10).

*Example (a).* Show that $t^3$ is of exponential order as $t \to \infty$.

We consider, with $b$ as yet unspecified,

(12) $$\operatorname{Lim}_{t \to \infty} (e^{-bt}t^3) = \operatorname{Lim}_{t \to \infty} \frac{t^3}{e^{bt}}.$$

If $b > 0$, the limit in (12) is of a type treated in calculus. In fact,

$$\operatorname{Lim}_{t \to \infty} \frac{t^3}{e^{bt}} = \operatorname{Lim}_{t \to \infty} \frac{3t^2}{be^{bt}} = \operatorname{Lim}_{t \to \infty} \frac{6t}{b^2 e^{bt}} = \operatorname{Lim}_{t \to \infty} \frac{6}{b^3 e^{bt}} = 0.$$

Therefore $t^3$ is of exponential order,

$$t^3 = O(e^{bt}), \qquad t \to \infty,$$

for any fixed positive $b$.

*Example (b).* Show that $\exp(t^2)$ is not of exponential order as $t \to \infty$.

Consider

(13) $$\operatorname{Lim}_{t \to \infty} \frac{\exp(t^2)}{\exp(bt)}.$$

If $b \leqq 0$, the limit in (13) is infinite. If $b > 0$,

$$\text{Lim}_{t \to \infty} \frac{\exp(t^2)}{\exp(bt)} = \text{Lim}_{t \to \infty} \exp[t(t - b)] = \infty.$$

Thus, no matter what fixed $b$ we use, the limit in (13) is infinite and $\exp(t^2)$ cannot be of exponential order.

The exercises at the end of the next section give additional opportunities for practice in determining whether or not a function is of exponential order.

## 6. *Functions of Class A*

For brevity we shall hereafter use the term "a function of class A" for any function which

(a) is sectionally continuous over every finite interval in the range $t \geqq 0$; and

(b) is of exponential order as $t \to \infty$.

We may then reword Theorem 2 as follows:

**THEOREM 3.**   *If $F(t)$ is a function of class A, $L\{F(t)\}$ exists.*

It is important to realize that Theorem 3 states only that for $L\{F(t)\}$ to exist it is sufficient that $F(t)$ be of class A. The condition is not necessary. A classic example showing that functions other than those of class A do have Laplace transforms is

$$F(t) = t^{-\frac{1}{2}}.$$

This function is not sectionally continuous in every finite interval in the range $t \geqq 0$ because $F \to \infty$ as $t \to 0^+$. But $t^{-\frac{1}{2}}$ is integrable from 0 to any positive $t_0$. Also $t^{-\frac{1}{2}} \to 0$ as $t \to \infty$, so $t^{-\frac{1}{2}}$ is of exponential order, with $M = 1$ and $b = 0$ in the inequality (3), page 8. Hence, by Theorem 1, page 8, $L\{t^{-\frac{1}{2}}\}$ exists.

Indeed, for $s > 0$,

$$L\{t^{-\frac{1}{2}}\} = \int_0^\infty e^{-st} t^{-\frac{1}{2}} \, dt,$$

in which the change of variable $t^{\frac{1}{2}} = \beta$ leads to

$$L\{t^{-\frac{1}{2}}\} = 2 \int_0^\infty \exp(-s\beta^2) \, d\beta, \qquad s > 0.$$

Another change of variable of integration, $s^{\frac{1}{2}}\beta = y$, yields

$$L\{t^{-\frac{1}{2}}\} = 2s^{-\frac{1}{2}} \int_0^\infty \exp(-y^2) \, dy, \qquad s > 0.$$

In elementary calculus* we found that $\int_0^\infty \exp(-y^2) \, dy = \frac{1}{2}\sqrt{\pi}$.

*E. D. Rainville, *Unified Calculus and Analytic Geometry*, New York, Macmillan, 1961, p. 531.

Therefore

(1) $$L\{t^{-\frac{1}{2}}\} = 2s^{-\frac{1}{2}} \cdot \tfrac{1}{2}\sqrt{\pi} = \left(\frac{\pi}{s}\right)^{\frac{1}{2}}, \qquad s > 0,$$

even though $t^{-\frac{1}{2}} \to \infty$ as $t \to 0^+$. Additional examples are easily constructed and we shall meet some of them later in the book.

If $F(t)$ is of class A, $F(t)$ is bounded over the range $0 \leqq t \leqq t_0$,

(2) $$|F(t)| < M_1, \qquad 0 \leqq t \leqq t_0.$$

But $F(t)$ is also of exponential order,

(3) $$|F(t)| < M_2 e^{bt}, \qquad t \geqq t_0.$$

If we choose $M$ as the larger of $M_1$ and $M_2$ and $c$ as the larger of $b$ and zero, we may write

(4) $$|F(t)| < M e^{ct}, \qquad t \geqq 0.$$

Therefore, for any function $F(t)$ of class A,

(5) $$\left| \int_0^\infty e^{-st}F(t)\, dt \right| < M \int_0^\infty e^{-st} \cdot e^{ct}\, dt = \frac{M}{s-c}, \qquad s > c.$$

Since the right member of (5) approaches zero as $s \to \infty$, we have proved the following useful result:

**THEOREM 4.** *If $F(t)$ is of class A and if $L\{F(t)\} = f(s)$,*

$$\operatorname*{Lim}_{s \to \infty} f(s) = 0.$$

From (5) we may also conclude the stronger result that the transform $f(s)$ of a function $F(t)$ of class A must be such that $sf(s)$ is bounded as $s \to \infty$.

### EXERCISES

1. Prove that if $F_1(t)$ and $F_2(t)$ are each of exponential order as $t \to \infty$, then $F_1(t) \cdot F_2(t)$ and $F_1(t) + F_2(t)$ are also of exponential order as $t \to \infty$.

2. Prove that if $F_1(t)$ and $F_2(t)$ are of class A, page 10, then $F_1(t) + F_2(t)$ and $F_1(t) \cdot F_2(t)$ are also of class A.

3. Show that $t^x$ is of exponential order as $t \to \infty$ for all real $x$.

In Exs. 4–17, show that the given function is of class A, page 10. In these exercises, $n$ denotes a nonnegative integer, $k$ any real number.

4. $\sin kt$.

5. $\cos kt$.

6. $\cosh kt$.

7. $\sinh kt$.

8. $t^n$.

9. $t^n e^{kt}$.

10. $t^n \sin kt$.

11. $t^n \cos kt$.

12. $t^n \sinh kt$.

13. $t^n \cosh kt$.

14. $\dfrac{\sin kt}{t}$.

15. $\dfrac{1 - \exp(-t)}{t}$.

16. $\dfrac{1 - \cos kt}{t}$.

17. $\dfrac{\cos t - \cosh t}{t}$.

## 7. *Transforms of Derivatives*

Any function of class A, page 10, has a Laplace transform but the derivative of such a function may, or may not, be of class A. For the function

$$F_1(t) = \sin[\exp(t)]$$

with derivative

$$F_1'(t) = \exp(t)\,\cos[\exp(t)],$$

both $F_1$ and $F_1'$ are of exponential order as $t \to \infty$. Here $F_1$ is bounded so it is of the order of $\exp(0 \cdot t)$; $F_1'$ is of the order of $\exp(t)$. On the other hand, the function

$$F_2(t) = \sin[\exp(t^2)]$$

with derivative

$$F_2'(t) = 2t\,\exp(t^2)\,\cos[\exp(t^2)]$$

is such that $F_2$ is of the order of $\exp(0 \cdot t)$, but $F_2'$ is not of exponential order. By Example (b), page 9,

$$\operatorname*{Lim}_{t\to\infty} \frac{\exp(t^2)}{\exp(bt)} = \infty$$

for any real $b$. Since the factors $2t \cos\,[\exp(t^2)]$ do not even approach zero as $t \to \infty$, the product $F_2' \exp(-ct)$ cannot be bounded as $t \to \infty$ no matter how large a fixed $c$ is chosen.

Therefore, in studying the transforms of derivatives we shall stipulate that the derivatives themselves be of class A.

If $F(t)$ is continuous for $t \geqq 0$ and of exponential order as $t \to \infty$, and if $F'(t)$ is of class A, the integral in

$$(1) \qquad L\{F'(t)\} = \int_0^\infty e^{-st}F'(t)\,dt$$

may be simplified by integration by parts with the choice exhibited in the table.

| $e^{-st}$ | $F'(t)\,dt$ |
|---|---|
| $-se^{-st}\,dt$ | $F(t)$ |

We thus obtain, for $s$ greater than some fixed $s_0$,

$$\int_0^\infty e^{-st}F'(t)\,dt = \left[ e^{-st}F(t) \right]_0^\infty + s\int_0^\infty e^{-st}F(t)\,dt,$$

or

$$(2) \qquad L\{F'(t)\} = -F(0) + sL\{F(t)\}.$$

**THEOREM 5.** *If $F(t)$ is continuous for $t \geqq 0$ and of exponential order as $t \to \infty$, and if $F'(t)$ is of class A, page 10, from $L\{F(t)\} = f(s)$, it follows that*

$$(3) \qquad L\{F'(t)\} = sf(s) - F(0).$$

In treating a differential equation of order $n$ we seek solutions for which the highest ordered derivative present is reasonably well behaved, say sectionally continuous. The integral of a sectionally continuous function is continuous. Hence we lose nothing by requiring continuity for all derivatives of order lower than $n$. The requirement that the various derivatives be of exponential order is forced upon us by our desire to use the Laplace transform as a tool. For our purposes iteration of Theorem 5 to obtain transforms of higher derivatives makes sense.

From (3) we obtain, if $F$, $F'$, $F''$ are suitably restricted,

$$L\{F''(t)\} = sL\{F'(t)\} - F'(0),$$

or

$$(4) \qquad L\{F''(t)\} = s^2f(s) - sF(0) - F'(0),$$

and the process can be repeated as many times as we wish.

**THEOREM 6.** *If $F(t)$, $F'(t)$, $\cdots$ , $F^{(n-1)}(t)$ are continuous for $t \geqq 0$ and of exponential order as $t \to \infty$, and if $F^{(n)}(t)$ is of class A, page 10, then from*

$$L\{F(t)\} = f(s)$$

*it follows that*

$$(5) \qquad L\{F^{(n)}(t)\} = s^nf(s) - \sum_{k=0}^{n-1} s^{n-1-k}F^{(k)}(0).$$

Thus

$$L\{F^{(3)}(t)\} = s^3f(s) - s^2F(0) - sF'(0) - F''(0),$$

$$L\{F^{(4)}(t)\} = s^4f(s) - s^3F(0) - s^2F'(0) - sF''(0) - F^{(3)}(0), \text{ etc.}$$

Theorem 6 is basic in employing the Laplace transform to solve linear differential equations with constant coefficients. The theorem permits us to transform such differential equations into algebraic ones.

The restriction that $F(t)$ be continuous can be relaxed, but discontinuities in $F(t)$ bring in additional terms in the transform of $F'(t)$. As an example, consider an $F(t)$ which is continuous for $t \geqq 0$ except for a finite jump at $t = t_1$, as in Fig. 2. If $F(t)$ is also of exponential order as $t \to \infty$ and if $F'(t)$ is of class A, we may write

$$L\{F'(t)\} = \int_0^\infty e^{-st}F'(t)\, dt$$

$$= \int_0^{t_1} e^{-st}F'(t)\, dt + \int_{t_1}^\infty e^{-st}F'(t)\, dt.$$

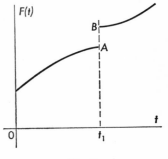

Fig. 2

Then integration by parts applied to the last two integrals yields

$$L\{F'(t)\} = \left[e^{-st}F(t)\right]_0^{t_1} + s\int_0^{t_1} e^{-st}F(t)\,dt + \left[e^{-st}F(t)\right]_{t_1}^{\infty} + s\int_{t_1}^{\infty} e^{-st}F(t)\,dt$$

$$= s\int_0^{\infty} e^{-st}F(t)\,dt + \exp(-st_1)F(t_1{}^-) - F(0) + 0 - \exp(-st_1)F(t_1{}^+)$$

$$= sL\{F(t)\} - F(0) - \exp(-st_1)[F(t_1{}^+) - F(t_1{}^-)].$$

In Fig. 2 the directed distance $AB$ is of length $[F(t_1{}^+) - F(t_1{}^-)]$.

**THEOREM 7.** *If $F(t)$ is of exponential order as $t \to \infty$ and $F(t)$ is continuous for $t \geqq 0$ except for a finite jump at $t = t_1$, and if $F'(t)$ is of class A, then from*

$$L\{F(t)\} = f(s)$$

*it follows that*

(6)          $$L\{F'(t)\} = sf(s) - F(0) - \exp(-st_1)[F(t_1{}^+) - F(t_1{}^-)].$$

If $F(t)$ has more than one finite discontinuity, additional terms, similar to the last term in (6), enter the formula for $L\{F'(t)\}$.

## 8. *Derivatives of Transforms*

For functions of class A, page 10, the methods of advanced calculus show that it is legitimate to differentiate the Laplace transform integral. That is, if $F(t)$ is of class A, from

(1)          $$f(s) = \int_0^{\infty} e^{-st}F(t)\,dt$$

it follows that

(2)          $$f'(s) = \int_0^{\infty} (-t)e^{-st}F(t)\,dt.$$

The integral on the right in (2) is the transform of the function $(-t)\,F(t)$.

**THEOREM 8.** *If $F(t)$ is a function of class A, it follows from*

$$L\{F(t)\} = f(s)$$

*that*

(3)          $$f'(s) = L\{-tF(t)\}.$$

When $F(t)$ is of class A, $(-t)^k F(t)$ is also of class A for any positive integer $k$.

**THEOREM 9.** *If $F(t)$ is of class A, it follows from $L\{F(t)\} = f(s)$ that for any positive integer $n$,*

(4)          $$\frac{d^n}{ds^n}f(s) = L\{(-t)^nF(t)\}.$$

These theorems are useful in several ways. One immediate application is to add to our list of transforms with very little labor. We know that

$$(5) \qquad \frac{k}{s^2 + k^2} = L\{\sin kt\},$$

and therefore, by Theorem 8,

$$\frac{-2ks}{(s^2 + k^2)^2} = L\{-t \sin kt\}.$$

Thus we obtain

$$(6) \qquad \frac{s}{(s^2 + k^2)^2} = L\left\{\frac{t}{2k} \sin kt\right\}.$$

From the known formula

$$\frac{s}{s^2 + k^2} = L\{\cos kt\}$$

we obtain, by differentiation with respect to $s$,

$$(7) \qquad \frac{k^2 - s^2}{(s^2 + k^2)^2} = L\{-t \cos kt\}.$$

Let us add to each side of (7) the corresponding member of

$$\frac{1}{s^2 + k^2} = L\left\{\frac{1}{k} \sin kt\right\}$$

to get

$$\frac{s^2 + k^2 + k^2 - s^2}{(s^2 + k^2)^2} = L\left\{\frac{1}{k} \sin kt - t \cos kt\right\},$$

from which it follows that

$$(8) \qquad \frac{1}{(s^2 + k^2)^2} = L\left\{\frac{1}{2k^3}(\sin kt - kt \cos kt)\right\}.$$

## 9. *The Gamma Function*

For the purpose of obtaining the Laplace transform of nonintegral powers of $t$, we need a function not usually discussed in elementary mathematics. The Gamma function $\Gamma(x)$ is defined* by

$$(1) \qquad \Gamma(x) = \int_0^\infty e^{-\beta}\beta^{x-1}\,d\beta, \qquad x > 0.$$

This is the definition used by Euler and it is equally good for complex $x$ in the region $\mathrm{Re}(x) > 0$. We restrict ourselves to real $x$.

Substitution of $(x + 1)$ for $x$ in (1) gives

$$(2) \qquad \Gamma(x + 1) = \int_0^\infty e^{-\beta}\beta^x\,d\beta.$$

---

*For another definition (that of Weierstrass in terms of infinite products) and for additional properties of the Gamma function, see E. D. Rainville, *Special Functions*, New York, Macmillan, 1960.

An integration by parts, integrating $e^{-\beta}d\beta$ and differentiating $\beta^x$, yields

$$(3) \qquad \Gamma(x+1) = \left[-e^{-\beta}\beta^x\right]_0^\infty + x\int_0^\infty e^{-\beta}\beta^{x-1}\,d\beta.$$

Since $x > 0$, $\beta^x \to 0$ as $\beta \to 0$. Since $x$ is fixed, $e^{-\beta}\beta^x \to 0$ as $\beta \to \infty$. Therefore (3) becomes

$$(4) \qquad \Gamma(x+1) = x\int_0^\infty e^{-\beta}\beta^{x-1}\,d\beta = x\Gamma(x).$$

THEOREM 10.  *For $x > 0$, $\Gamma(x+1) = x\Gamma(x)$.*

Suppose $n$ is a positive integer.  Iteration of Theorem 10 gives us

$$\begin{aligned}
\Gamma(n+1) &= n\Gamma(n) \\
&= n(n-1)\Gamma(n-1) \\
&\quad \cdots \\
&= n(n-1)(n-2)\cdots 2\cdot 1\cdot\Gamma(1). \\
&= n!\Gamma(1).
\end{aligned}$$

But, by definition,

$$\Gamma(1) = \int_0^\infty e^{-\beta}\beta^0\,d\beta = \left[-e^{-\beta}\right]_0^\infty = 1.$$

THEOREM 11.  *For positive integral $n$, $\Gamma(n+1) = n!$.*

In the integral for $\Gamma(x+1)$ in (2) let us put $\beta = st$ with $s > 0$ and $t$ as the new variable of integration.  This yields, since $t \to 0$ as $\beta \to 0$ and $t \to \infty$ as $\beta \to \infty$,

$$(5) \qquad \Gamma(x+1) = \int_0^\infty e^{-st}s^x t^x s\,dt = s^{x+1}\int_0^\infty e^{-st}t^x\,dt,$$

which is valid for $x + 1 > 0$.  We thus obtain

$$\frac{\Gamma(x+1)}{s^{x+1}} = \int_0^\infty e^{-st}t^x\,dt, \qquad s > 0,\ x > -1,$$

which in our Laplace transform notation says that

$$(6) \qquad L\{t^x\} = \frac{\Gamma(x+1)}{s^{x+1}}, \qquad s > 0,\quad x > -1.$$

By Theorem 11 this agrees (naturally, since both are correct) with our formula for the transform of an integral power of $t$.

If in (6) we put $x = -\frac{1}{2}$, we get

$$L\{t^{-\frac{1}{2}}\} = \frac{\Gamma(\frac{1}{2})}{s^{\frac{1}{2}}}.$$

But we already know that $L\{t^{-\frac{1}{2}}\} = \left(\dfrac{\pi}{s}\right)^{\frac{1}{2}}$. Hence

$$(7) \qquad \Gamma(\tfrac{1}{2}) = \sqrt{\pi}.$$

## 10. *Periodic Functions*

Suppose the function $F(t)$ is periodic with period $\omega$:

$$(1) \qquad\qquad F(t + \omega) = F(t).$$

The function is completely determined by (1) once the nature of $F(t)$ throughout one period, $0 \leq t < \omega$, is given. If $F(t)$ has a Laplace transform,

$$(2) \qquad\qquad L\{F(t)\} = \int_0^\infty e^{-st}F(t)\, dt,$$

the integral can be written as a sum of integrals,

$$(3) \qquad\qquad L\{F(t)\} = \sum_{n=0}^\infty \int_{n\omega}^{(n+1)\omega} e^{-st}F(t)\, dt.$$

Let us put $t = n\omega + \beta$. Then (3) becomes

$$L\{F(t)\} = \sum_{n=0}^\infty \int_0^\omega \exp(-sn\omega - s\beta)F(\beta + n\omega)d\beta.$$

But $F(\beta + n\omega) = F(\beta)$, by iteration of (1). Hence

$$(4) \qquad\qquad L\{F(t)\} = \sum_{n=0}^\infty \exp(-sn\omega)\int_0^\omega \exp(-s\beta)F(\beta)d\beta.$$

The integral on the right in (4) is independent of $n$ and we can sum the series on the right;

$$\sum_{n=0}^\infty \exp(-sn\omega) = \sum_{n=0}^\infty [\exp(-s\omega)]^n = \frac{1}{1 - e^{-s\omega}}.$$

**THEOREM 12.** *If $F(t)$ has a Laplace transform and if $F(t + \omega) = F(t)$, then*

$$(5) \qquad\qquad L\{F(t)\} = \frac{\int_0^\omega e^{-s\beta}F(\beta)d\beta}{1 - e^{-s\omega}}.$$

Next suppose that a function $H(t)$ has a period $2c$ and that we demand that $H(t)$ be zero throughout the right half of each period. That is,

$$(6) \qquad\qquad H(t + 2c) = H(t),$$

$$(7) \qquad\qquad \begin{aligned} H(t) &= g(t), & 0 \leq t < c, \\ &= 0, & c \leq t < 2c. \end{aligned}$$

Then we say that $H(t)$ is a half-wave rectification of $g(t)$. Using (5) we may conclude that for the $H(t)$ defined by (6) and (7),

$$(8) \qquad\qquad L\{H(t)\} = \frac{\int_0^c \exp(-s\beta)g(\beta)d\beta}{1 - \exp(-2cs)}.$$

*Example* (a).   Find the transform of the function $\psi(t, c)$ shown in Fig. 3 and defined by

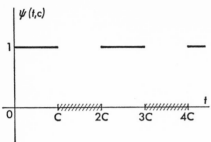

(9)   $\psi(t, c) = 1,$      $0 < t < c,$
            $= 0,$      $c < t < 2c;$

(10)      $\psi(t + 2c, c) = \psi(t, c).$

We may use equation (8) above and the fact that

$$\int_0^c \exp(-s\beta)d\beta = \frac{1 - \exp(-sc)}{s}$$

**Fig. 3**

to conclude that

(11)      $L\{\psi(t, c)\} = \dfrac{1}{s} \cdot \dfrac{1 - \exp(-sc)}{1 - \exp(-2sc)} = \dfrac{1}{s} \cdot \dfrac{1}{1 + \exp(-sc)}.$

*Example* (b). Find the transform of the square wave function $Q(t, c)$ shown in Fig. 4 and defined by

(12)   $Q(t, c) = 1,$      $0 < t < c,$
            $= -1,$      $c < t < 2c;$

(13)   $Q(t + 2c, c) = Q(t, c).$

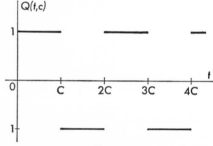

**Fig. 4**

This transform can be obtained by using Theorem 12, but also

(14)   $Q(t, c) = 2\psi(t, c) - 1.$

Hence, from (11),

(15)      $L\{Q(t, c)\} = \dfrac{1}{s}\left[\dfrac{2}{1 + \exp(-sc)} - 1\right] = \dfrac{1}{s} \cdot \dfrac{1 - \exp(-sc)}{1 + \exp(-sc)}.$

By multiplying numerator and denominator of the last fraction above by $\exp(\frac{1}{2}sc)$, we may put (15) in the form

(16)                $L\{Q(t, c)\} = \dfrac{1}{s} \tanh \dfrac{cs}{2}.$

**EXERCISES**

**1.** Show that $L\{t^{\frac{1}{2}}\} = \dfrac{1}{2s}\left(\dfrac{\pi}{s}\right)^{\frac{1}{2}},$   $s > 0.$

**2.** Show that $L\{t^{\frac{5}{2}}\} = \dfrac{15}{8s^3}\left(\dfrac{\pi}{s}\right)^{\frac{1}{2}},$   $s > 0.$

**3.** Use equation (4), page 13, to derive $L\{\sin kt\}.$

**4.** Use equation (4), page 13, to derive $L\{\cos kt\}$.

**5.** Check the known transforms of $\sin kt$ and $\cos kt$ against one another by using Theorem 5, page 12.

**6.** If $n$ is a positive integer, obtain $L\{t^n e^{kt}\}$ from the known $L\{e^{kt}\}$ by using Theorem 9, page 14.

$$Ans. \ \frac{n!}{(s-k)^{n+1}}, \quad s > k.$$

**7.** Find $L\{t^2 \sin kt\}$.

$$Ans. \ \frac{2k(3s^2 - k^2)}{(s^2 + k^2)^3}, \quad s > 0.$$

**8.** Find $L\{t^2 \cos kt\}$.

$$Ans. \ \frac{2s(s^2 - 3k^2)}{(s^2 + k^2)^3}, \quad s > 0.$$

**9.** For the function

$$F(t) = t + 1, \quad 0 \le t \le 2,$$
$$= 3, \quad t > 2,$$

graph $F(t)$ and $F'(t)$. Find $L\{F(t)\}$. Find $L\{F'(t)\}$ in two ways.

$$Ans. \ L\{F'(t)\} = s^{-1}(1 - e^{-2s}), \quad s > 0.$$

**10.** For the function

$$H(t) = t + 1, \quad 0 \le t \le 2,$$
$$= 6, \quad t > 2,$$

parallel Ex. 9 above.

**11.** Define a triangular wave function $T(t, c)$ by

$$T(t, c) = t, \quad 0 \le t \le c,$$
$$= 2c - t, \quad c < t < 2c;$$
$$T(t + 2c, c) = T(t, c).$$

Sketch $T(t, c)$ and find its Laplace transform.

$$Ans. \ \frac{1}{s^2} \tanh \frac{cs}{2}.$$

**12.** Show that the derivative of the function $T(t, c)$ of Ex. 11 is, except at certain points, the function $Q(t, c)$ of Example (b), §10. Obtain $L\{T(t, c)\}$ from $L\{Q(t, c)\}$.

**13.** Sketch a half-wave rectification of the function $\sin \omega t$, as described below and find its transform:

$$F(t) = \sin \omega t, \quad 0 \le t \le \frac{\pi}{\omega},$$
$$= 0, \quad \frac{\pi}{\omega} < t < \frac{2\pi}{\omega};$$
$$F\left(t + \frac{2\pi}{\omega}\right) = F(t).$$

$$Ans. \ \frac{\omega}{s^2 + \omega^2} \cdot \frac{1}{1 - \exp\left(-\frac{s\pi}{\omega}\right)}.$$

**14.** Find $L\{F(t)\}$ where $F(t) = t$ for $0 < t < \omega$ and $F(t + \omega) = F(t)$.

$$Ans. \;\; \frac{1}{s^2} - \frac{\omega}{s}\frac{\exp(-s\omega)}{1 - \exp(-s\omega)} = \frac{1}{s^2} + \frac{\omega}{2s}\left(1 - \coth\frac{\omega s}{2}\right).$$

**15.** Prove that if $L\{F(t)\} = f(s)$ and if $\dfrac{F(t)}{t}$ is of class A,

$$L\left\{\frac{F(t)}{t}\right\} = \int_s^\infty f(\beta)\,d\beta.$$

*Hint:*   Use Theorem 8, page 14.

# Inverse Transforms

## 11. Definition of an Inverse Transform

Suppose we have a differential equation with boundary conditions from which the function $F(t)$ is to be determined. The Laplace operator $L$ is used to transform the original problem into a new problem from which the transform $f(s)$ is to be found. If the Laplace transformation is to be effective, the new problem must be simpler than the original problem. We first find $f(s)$ and then must obtain $F(t)$ from $f(s)$. It is therefore desirable to develop methods for finding the object function $F(t)$ when its transform $f(s)$ is known.

If

$$(1) \qquad L\{F(t)\} = f(s),$$

we say that $F(t)$ is an *inverse Laplace transform*, or an inverse transform, of $f(s)$ and we write

$$(2) \qquad F(t) = L^{-1}\{f(s)\}.$$

Since (1) means that

$$(3) \qquad \int_0^\infty e^{-st}F(t)\,dt = f(s),$$

it follows at once that an inverse transform is not unique. For example, if $F_1(t)$ and $F_2(t)$ are identical except at a discrete set of points and differ at those points, the value of the integral in (3) is the same for the two functions; their transforms are identical.

Let us employ the term *null function* for any function $N(t)$ for which

$$(4) \qquad \int_0^{t_0} N(t)\,dt = 0$$

for every positive $t_0$. Lerch's theorem (not proved here) states that: If $L\{F_1(t)\} = L\{F_2(t)\}$, then $F_1(t) - F_2(t) = N(t)$. That is, an inverse Laplace transform is unique except for the addition of an arbitrary null function.

The only continuous null function is zero. If an $f(s)$ has a continuous inverse $F(t)$, then $F(t)$ is the only continuous inverse of $f(s)$. If $f(s)$ has an inverse $F_1(t)$ continuous over a specified closed interval, every inverse which is also continuous over that interval is identical with $F_1(t)$ on that interval. Essentially, inverses of the same $f(s)$ differ at most at their points of discontinuity.

In applications, failure of uniqueness by addition of a null function is not vital because the effect of that null function on physical properties of the solution is null. In the problems we treat, the inverse $F(t)$ is required either to be continuous for $t \geqq 0$ or to be sectionally continuous with the values of $F(t)$ at the points of discontinuity specified by the problem. The $F(t)$ is then unique.

A crude, but sometimes effective, method for finding inverse Laplace transforms is to construct a table of transforms (page 101) and then to use it in reverse to find inverse transforms.

We know from Ex. 1, page 5, that

$$(5) \qquad L\{\cos kt\} = \frac{s}{s^2 + k^2}.$$

Therefore

$$(6) \qquad L^{-1}\left\{\frac{s}{s^2 + k^2}\right\} = \cos kt.$$

We shall refine the above method, and actually make it quite powerful, by developing theorems by which a given $f(s)$ may be expanded into component parts whose inverses are known (found in the table). Other theorems will permit us to write $f(s)$ in alternate forms which yield the desired inverse. The most fundamental of such theorems is one which states that the inverse transformation is a linear operation.

**THEOREM 13.** *If $c_1$ and $c_2$ are constants,*

$$L^{-1}\{c_1 f_1(s) + c_2 f_2(s)\} = c_1 L^{-1}\{f_1(s)\} + c_2 L^{-1}\{f_2(s)\}.$$

Next let us prove a simple, but extremely useful, theorem on the manipulation of inverse transforms. From

$$(7) \qquad f(s) = \int_0^\infty e^{-st} F(t)\, dt,$$

we obtain

$$f(s - a) = \int_0^\infty e^{-(s-a)t} F(t)\, dt$$

$$= \int_0^\infty e^{-st}[e^{at} F(t)]\, dt.$$

Thus, from $L^{-1}\{f(s)\} = F(t)$ it follows that $L^{-1}\{f(s - a)\} = e^{at} F(t)$ or

(8) $$L^{-1}\{f(s-a)\} = e^{at}L^{-1}\{f(s)\} .$$

Equation (8) may be rewritten with the exponential transferred to the other side of the equation. We thus obtain the following result.

THEOREM 14.   $L^{-1}\{f(s)\} = e^{-at}L^{-1}\{f(s-a)\}.$

*Example* (a).   Find $L^{-1}\left\{\dfrac{15}{s^2 + 4s + 13}\right\}.$

First complete the square in the denominator:

$$L^{-1}\left\{\frac{15}{s^2 + 4s + 13}\right\} = L^{-1}\left\{\frac{15}{(s+2)^2 + 9}\right\}.$$

Since we know that $L^{-1}\left\{\dfrac{k}{s^2 + k^2}\right\} = \sin kt,$ we proceed as follows:

$$L^{-1}\left\{\frac{15}{s^2 + 4s + 13}\right\} = 5L^{-1}\left\{\frac{3}{(s+2)^2 + 9}\right\} = 5e^{-2t}L^{-1}\left\{\frac{3}{s^2 + 9}\right\} = 5e^{-2t}\sin 3t,$$

in which we have used Theorem 14.

*Example* (b).   Evaluate $L^{-1}\left\{\dfrac{s+1}{s^2 + 6s + 25}\right\}.$

We write

$$L^{-1}\left\{\frac{s+1}{s^2 + 6s + 25}\right\} = L^{-1}\left\{\frac{s+1}{(s+3)^2 + 16}\right\}$$

$$= e^{-3t}L^{-1}\left\{\frac{s-2}{s^2 + 16}\right\}$$

$$= e^{-3t}\left[L^{-1}\left\{\frac{s}{s^2 + 16}\right\} - \tfrac{1}{2}L^{-1}\left\{\frac{4}{s^2 + 16}\right\}\right]$$

$$= e^{-3t}(\cos 4t - \tfrac{1}{2}\sin 4t) .$$

## EXERCISES

In Exs. 1–10, obtain $L^{-1}\{f(s)\}$ from the given $f(s)$.

1. $\dfrac{1}{s^2 + 2s + 5}.$                                 *Ans.* $\tfrac{1}{2}e^{-t}\sin 2t.$

2. $\dfrac{1}{s^2 - 6s + 10}.$                                 *Ans.* $e^{3t}\sin t.$

3. $\dfrac{s}{s^2 + 2s + 5}.$                                 *Ans.* $e^{-t}(\cos 2t - \tfrac{1}{2}\sin 2t).$

4. $\dfrac{s}{s^2 - 6s + 13}.$                                 *Ans.* $e^{3t}(\cos 2t + \tfrac{3}{2}\sin 2t).$

5. $\dfrac{1}{s^2 + 8s + 16}.$                                 *Ans.* $te^{-4t}.$

**6.** $\dfrac{s}{s^2 + 8s + 16}$. Ans. $e^{-4t}(1 - 4t)$.

**7.** $\dfrac{s - 5}{s^2 + 6s + 13}$. Ans. $e^{-3t}(\cos 2t - 4 \sin 2t)$.

**8.** $\dfrac{2s - 1}{s^2 + 4s + 29}$. Ans. $e^{-2t}(2 \cos 5t - \sin 5t)$.

**9.** $\dfrac{3s + 1}{(s + 1)^4}$. Ans. $e^{-t}\left(\dfrac{3}{2} t^2 - \dfrac{1}{3} t^3\right)$.

**10.** $\dfrac{s^2}{(s + 2)^3}$. Ans. $e^{-2t}(1 - 4t + 2t^2)$.

**11.** Show that for $n$ a nonnegative integer

$$L^{-1}\left\{\frac{1}{(s + a)^{n+1}}\right\} = \frac{t^n e^{-at}}{n!}.$$

**12.** Show that for $m > -1$,

$$L^{-1}\left\{\frac{1}{(s + a)^{m+1}}\right\} = \frac{t^m e^{-at}}{\Gamma(m + 1)}.$$

**13.** Show that

$$L^{-1}\left\{\frac{1}{(s + a)^2 + b^2}\right\} = \frac{1}{b} e^{-at} \sin bt.$$

**14.** Show that

$$L^{-1}\left\{\frac{s}{(s + a)^2 + b^2}\right\} = \frac{1}{b} e^{-at} (b \cos bt - a \sin bt).$$

**15.** For $a > 0$, show that from $L^{-1}\{f(s)\} = F(t)$ it follows that

$$L^{-1}\{f(as)\} = \frac{1}{a} F\left(\frac{t}{a}\right).$$

**16.** For $a > 0$, show that from $L^{-1}\{f(s)\} = F(t)$ it follows that

$$L^{-1}\{f(as + b)\} = \frac{1}{a} \exp\left(-\frac{bt}{a}\right) F\left(\frac{t}{a}\right).$$

## 12. *A Step Function*

Applications frequently deal with situations which change abruptly at specified times. We need a notation for a function which will suppress a given term up to certain value of $t$ and insert the term for all larger $t$. The function we are about to introduce leads us to a powerful tool in the constructing of inverse transforms.

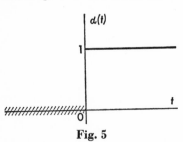

**Fig. 5**

Let us define the function $\alpha(t)$ by

$$(1) \qquad \alpha(t) = 0, \qquad t < 0.$$
$$= 1, \qquad t \geqq 0.$$

The graph of $\alpha(t)$ is shown in Fig. 5.

The definition (1) says that $\alpha(t)$ is zero when the argument is negative and $\alpha(t)$ is unity when the argument is positive or is zero. It follows that

(2) $$\alpha(t - c) = 0, \qquad t < c,$$
$$= 1, \qquad t \geqq c.$$

The $\alpha$ function permits easy designation of the result of translating the graph of $F(t)$. If the graph of

(3) $$y = F(t), \qquad t \geqq 0,$$

is as shown in Fig. 6, the graph of

(4) $$y = \alpha(t - c) F(t - c), \qquad t \geqq c,$$

is that shown in Fig. 7. Furthermore, if $F(x)$ is defined for $-c \leqq x < 0$, $F(t - c)$ is defined for $0 \leqq t < c$ and the $y$ of (4) is zero for $0 \leqq t < c$ because

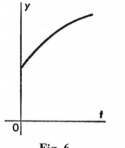

Fig. 6

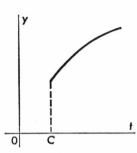

Fig. 7

of the negative argument in $\alpha(t - c)$. Notice that the values of $F(x)$ for negative $x$ have no bearing on this result because each value is multiplied by zero (from the $\alpha$); only the existence of $F$ for negative arguments is needed.

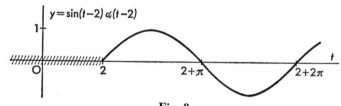

Fig. 8

The Laplace transform of $\alpha(t - c) F(t - c)$ is related to that of $F(t)$. Consider

$$L\{\alpha(t - c)F(t - c)\} = \int_0^\infty e^{-st}\alpha(t - c)F(t - c)\, dt.$$

Since $\alpha(t - c) = 0$ for $0 \leqq t < c$ and $\alpha(t - c) = 1$ for $t \geqq c$, we get

$$L\{\alpha(t - c)F(t - c)\} = \int_c^\infty e^{-st}F(t - c)\, dt.$$

Now put $t - c = v$ in the integral to obtain

$$L\{\alpha(t - c)F(t - c)\} = \int_0^\infty e^{-s(c+v)}F(v)\,dv$$

$$= e^{-cs}\int_0^\infty e^{-sv}F(v)\,dv.$$

Since a definite integral is independent of the variable of integration,

$$\int_0^\infty e^{-sv}F(v)\,dv = \int_0^\infty e^{-st}F(t)\,dt = L\{F(t)\} = f(s)\cdot$$

Therefore we have shown that

(5)        $$L\{\alpha(t - c)\,F(t - c)\} = e^{-cs}L\{F(t)\} = e^{-cs}f(s).$$

Equation (5) is more useful when written as a theorem on the inverse transform.

**THEOREM 15.**   *If $L^{-1}\{f(s)\} = F(t)$, if $c \geqq 0$, and if $F(t)$ be assigned values (no matter what ones) for $-c \leqq t < 0$,*

(6)        $$L^{-1}\{e^{-cs}f(s)\} = F(t - c)\alpha(t - c)\ .$$

*Example (a).*   Find $L\{y(t)\}$ where (Fig. 9)

$$y(t) = t^2, \qquad 0 < t < 2,$$
$$= 6, \qquad t > 2.$$

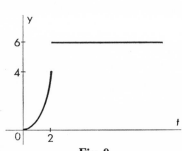

**Fig. 9**

Here direct use of the definition of a transform yields

$$L\{y(t)\} = \int_0^2 t^2 e^{-st}\,dt + \int_2^\infty 6e^{-st}\,dt.$$

Although the above integrations are not difficult, one of them may (or may not, depending on the skill of the operator) involve two integrations by parts.   We prefer to use the $\alpha$ function.

Since $\alpha(t - 2) = 0$ for $t < 2$ and $\alpha(t - 2) = 1$ for $t \geqq 2$, we build the $y(t)$ in the following way.   The crude trial

$$y_1 = t^2$$

works for $0 < t < 2$, but we wish to knock out the $t^2$ when $t > 2$.   Hence we write

$$y_2 = t^2 - t^2\alpha(t - 2)\ .$$

This gives $t^2$ for $t < 2$ and zero for $t > 2$.   Then we add the term $6\alpha(t - 2)$ and finally arrive at

(7)        $$y(t) = t^2 - t^2\alpha(t - 2) + 6\alpha(t - 2).$$

The $y$ of (7) is the $y$ of our example and, of course, it can be written at once after a little practice with the $\alpha$ function. No intermediate steps such as forming $y_1$ and $y_2$ need be used.

Unfortunately, the $y$ of (7) is not yet in the best form for our purpose. The theorem we wish to use gives us

$$L\{F(t-c)\alpha(t-c)\} = e^{-cs}f(s) .$$

Therefore we must have the coefficient of $\alpha(t-2)$ expressed as a function of $(t-2)$. Since

$$-t^2 + 6 = -(t^2 - 4t + 4) - 4(t-2) + 2,$$

(8) $$y(t) = t^2 - (t-2)^2\alpha(t-2) - 4(t-2)\alpha(t-2) + 2\alpha(t-2)$$

from which it follows at once that

$$L\{y(t)\} = \frac{2}{s^3} - \frac{2e^{-2s}}{s^3} - \frac{4e^{-2s}}{s^2} + \frac{2e^{-2s}}{s}.$$

*Example (b).* Find and sketch a function $g(t)$ for which

$$g(t) = L^{-1}\left\{\frac{3}{s} - \frac{4e^{-s}}{s^2} + \frac{4e^{-3s}}{s^2}\right\}.$$

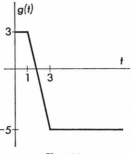

Fig. 10

We know that $L^{-1}\left\{\frac{4}{s^2}\right\} = 4t.$ By Theorem 15 we then get

$$L^{-1}\left\{\frac{4e^{-s}}{s^2}\right\} = 4(t-1)\alpha(t-1)$$

and

$$L^{-1}\left\{\frac{4e^{-3s}}{s^2}\right\} = 4(t-3)\alpha(t-3).$$

We may therefore write

(9) $$g(t) = 3 - 4(t-1)\alpha(t-1) + 4(t-3)\alpha(t-3).$$

To write $g(t)$ without the $\alpha$ function, consider first the interval $0 \leq t < 1$ in which $\alpha(t-1) = 0$ and $\alpha(t-3) = 0$. We find

(10) $$g(t) = 3, \qquad 0 \leq t < 1.$$

For $1 \leq t < 3$, $\alpha(t-1) = 1$, and $\alpha(t-3) = 0$. Hence

(11) $$g(t) = 3 - 4(t-1) = 7 - 4t, \qquad 1 \leq t < 3.$$

For $t \geq 3$, $\alpha(t-1) = 1$ and $\alpha(t-3) = 1$, so

(12) $$g(t) = 3 - 4(t-1) + 4(t-3) = -5, \qquad t \geq 3.$$

Equations (10, 11), and (12) are equivalent to equation (9). The graph of $g(t)$ is shown in Fig. 10.

## EXERCISES

In Exs. 1–8, express the given $F(t)$ in terms of the $\alpha$ function and find $L\{F(t)\}$.

**1.** $F(t) = 2, \quad 0 < t < 1,$
$\qquad = t, \qquad t > 1.$

Ans. $\dfrac{2}{s} + e^{-s}\left(\dfrac{1}{s^2} - \dfrac{1}{s}\right).$

**2.** $F(t) = 6, \quad 0 < t < 4,$
$\qquad = 2t + 1, \quad t > 4.$

Ans. $\dfrac{6}{s} + e^{-4s}\left(\dfrac{2}{s^2} + \dfrac{3}{s}\right).$

**3.** $F(t) = t^2, \quad 0 < t < 1,$
$\qquad = 4, \qquad t > 1.$

Ans. $\dfrac{2}{s^3} + e^{-s}\left(\dfrac{3}{s} - \dfrac{2}{s^2} - \dfrac{2}{s^3}\right).$

**4.** $F(t) = t^2, \quad 0 < t < 2,$
$\qquad = 4, \qquad 2 \le t \le 4,$
$\qquad = 0, \qquad t > 4.$

Ans. $\dfrac{2}{s^3} - e^{-2s}\left(\dfrac{4}{s^2} + \dfrac{2}{s^3}\right) - \dfrac{4}{s} e^{-4s}.$

**5.** $F(t) = t^2, \quad 0 < t < 2,$
$\qquad = t - 1, 2 < t < 3,$
$\qquad = 7, \qquad t > 3.$

Ans. $\dfrac{2}{s^3} - e^{-2s}\left(\dfrac{3}{s} + \dfrac{3}{s^2} + \dfrac{2}{s^3}\right) + e^{-3s}\left(\dfrac{5}{s} - \dfrac{1}{s^2}\right).$

**6.** $F(t) = e^{-t}, \quad 0 < t < 2,$
$\qquad = 0, \qquad t > 2.$

Ans. $\dfrac{1 - \exp(-2s - 2)}{s + 1}.$

**7.** $F(t) = \sin 3t, \quad 0 < t < \frac{1}{2}\pi,$
$\qquad = 0, \qquad t > \frac{1}{2}\pi.$

Ans. $\dfrac{3 + s \exp(-\frac{1}{2}\pi s)}{s^2 + 9}.$

**8.** $F(t) = \sin 3t, \quad 0 < t < \pi,$
$\qquad = 0, \qquad t > \pi.$

Ans. $\dfrac{3(1 + e^{-\pi s})}{s^2 + 9}.$

**9.** Find and sketch an inverse Laplace transform of

$$\frac{5e^{-3s}}{s} - \frac{e^{-s}}{s}.$$

Ans. $F(t) = 5\alpha(t - 3) - \alpha(t - 1).$

**10.** Evaluate $L^{-1}\left\{\dfrac{e^{-4s}}{(s + 2)^3}\right\}.$

Ans. $\frac{1}{2}(t - 4)^2 \exp[-2(t - 4)]\alpha(t - 4).$

**11.** If $F(t)$ is to be continuous for $t \ge 0$ and

$$F(t) = L^{-1}\left\{\frac{e^{-3s}}{(s + 1)^3}\right\}$$

evaluate $F(2)$, $F(5)$, $F(7)$.

Ans. $F(2) = 0$, $F(5) = 2e^{-2}$, $F(7) = 8e^{-4}.$

**12.** If $F(t)$ is to be continuous for $t \ge 0$ and

$$F(t) = L^{-1}\left\{\frac{(1 - e^{-2s})(1 - 3e^{-2s})}{s^2}\right\},$$

evaluate $F(1,)$ $F(3)$, $F(5)$.

Ans. $F(1) = 1$, $F(3) = -1$, $F(5) = -4.$

**13.** Prove that $\psi(t, c) = \sum\limits_{n=0}^{\infty} (-1)^n \alpha(t - nc)$ is the same function as was used in Example (a), §10. Note that, for any specific $t$, the series is finite; no question of convergence is involved.

**14.** Obtain the transform of the half-wave rectification $F(t)$ of $\sin t$ by writing

$$F(t) = \sin t \; \psi \; (t, \pi)$$

in terms of the $\psi$ of Ex. 13 above. Use the fact that $(-1)^n \sin t = \sin(t - n\pi)$. Check your result with that in Ex. 13, page 19.

## 13. *A Convolution Theorem*

We now seek a formula for the inverse transform of a product of transforms. Given

(1)  $\qquad L^{-1}\{f(s)\} = F(t), \qquad L^{-1}\{g(s)\} = G(t) \, ,$

in which $F(t)$ and $G(t)$ are assumed to be functions of class A, we shall obtain a formula for

(2)  $\qquad L^{-1}\{f(s) \; g(s)\} \cdot$

Since $f(s)$ is the transform of $F(t)$, we may write

(3)  $$f(s) = \int_0^\infty e^{-st} F(t) \; dt.$$

Since $g(s)$ is the transform of $G(t)$,

(4)  $$g(s) = \int_0^\infty e^{-s\beta} G(\beta) \; d\beta,$$

in which, to avoid confusion, we have used $\beta$ (rather than $t$) as the variable of integration in the definite integral.

By equation (4), we have

(5)  $$f(s)g(s) = \int_0^\infty e^{-s\beta} f(s) G(\beta) \; d\beta.$$

On the right in (5) we encounter the product $e^{-s\beta} f(s)$. By Theorem 15, page 26, we know that from

(6)  $\qquad L^{-1}\{f(s)\} = F(t)$

it follows that

(7)  $\qquad L^{-1}\{e^{-s\beta} f(s)\} = F(t - \beta)\alpha(t - \beta) \, ,$

in which $\alpha$ is the step function of §12. Equation (7) means that

(8)  $$e^{-s\beta} f(s) = \int_0^\infty e^{-st} F(t - \beta)\alpha(t - \beta) \; dt.$$

With the aid of (8) we may put equation (5) in the form

(9)  $$f(s)g(s) = \int_0^\infty \int_0^\infty e^{-st} G(\beta) F(t - \beta)\alpha(t - \beta) \; dt \; d\beta.$$

Since $\alpha(t - \beta) = 0$ for $0 < t < \beta$ and $\alpha(t - \beta) = 1$ for $t \geqq \beta$, equation (9) may be rewritten as

$$(10) \qquad f(s)g(s) = \int_0^\infty \int_\beta^\infty e^{-st}G(\beta)F(t - \beta) \, dt \, d\beta.$$

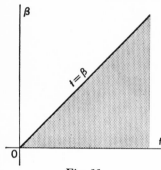

**Fig. 11**

In (10) the integration in the $t\beta$-plane covers the shaded region shown in Fig. 11. The elements are summed from $t = \beta$ to $t = \infty$ and then from $\beta = 0$ to $\beta = \infty$.

By the methods of advanced calculus it can be shown that, because $F(t)$ and $G(t)$ are functions of class A, it is legitimate to interchange the order of integration on the right in equation (10). From Fig. 11 we see that in the new order of integration the elements are to be summed from $\beta = 0$ to $\beta = t$ and then from $t = 0$ to $t = \infty$. We thus obtain

$$f(s)g(s) = \int_0^\infty \int_0^t e^{-st}G(\beta)F(t - \beta) \, d\beta \, dt,$$

or

$$(11) \qquad f(s)g(s) = \int_0^\infty e^{-st}\left[\int_0^t G(\beta)F(t - \beta) \, d\beta\right] dt.$$

Since the right member of (11) is precisely the Laplace transform of

$$\int_0^t G(\beta)F(t - \beta)d\beta,$$

we have arrived at the desired result, which is called the convolution theorem for the Laplace transform.

**THEOREM 16.** *If $L^{-1}\{f(s)\} = F(t)$, if $L^{-1}\{g(s)\} = G(t)$, and if $F(t)$ and $G(t)$ are functions of class A, page 10, then*

$$(12) \qquad L^{-1}\{f(s)g(s)\} = \int_0^t G(\beta)F(t - \beta) \, d\beta.$$

It is easy to show that the right member of equation (12) is also a function of class A.

Of course $F$ and $G$ are interchangeable in (12) since $f$ and $g$ enter (12) symmetrically. We may replace (12) by

$$(13) \qquad L^{-1}\{f(s)g(s)\} = \int_0^t F(\beta)G(t - \beta) \, d\beta,$$

a result which also follows from (12) by a change of variable of integration.

*Example.*   Evaluate $L^{-1}\left\{\dfrac{f(s)}{s}\right\}$.

Let $L^{-1}\{f(s)\} = F(t)$.   Since $L^{-1}\left\{\dfrac{1}{s}\right\} = 1$, we use Theorem 16 to conclude that

$$L^{-1}\left\{\frac{f(s)}{s}\right\} = \int_0^t F(\beta)\, d\beta.$$

## 14. *Partial Fractions*

In using the Laplace transform to solve differential equations, we often need to obtain the inverse transform of a rational fraction

$$(1) \qquad \frac{N(s)}{D(s)}.$$

The numerator and denominator in (1) are polynomials in $s$ and the degree of $D(s)$ is larger than the degree of $N(s)$.   The fraction (1) has the partial fractions expansion used in calculus.*   Because of the linearity of the inverse operator $L^{-1}$, the partial fractions expansion of (1) permits us to replace a complicated problem in obtaining an inverse transform by a set of simpler problems.

*Example (a).*   Obtain $L^{-1}\left\{\dfrac{s^2 - 6}{s^3 + 4s^2 + 3s}\right\}$.

Since the denominator is a product of distinct linear factors, we know that constants $A$, $B$, $C$ exist such that

$$\frac{s^2 - 6}{s^3 + 4s^2 + 3s} = \frac{s^2 - 6}{s(s + 1)(s + 3)} = \frac{A}{s} + \frac{B}{s + 1} + \frac{C}{s + 3}.$$

Multiplying each term by the lowest common denominator, we obtain the identity

$$(2) \qquad s^2 - 6 = A(s + 1)(s + 3) + Bs(s + 3) + Cs(s + 1),$$

from which we need to determine $A$, $B$, and $C$.   Using the values $s = 0$, $-1$, $-3$ successively in (2), we get

$$s = 0: \qquad\qquad -6 = A(1)(3),$$
$$s = -1: \qquad\qquad -5 = B(-1)(2),$$
$$s = -3: \qquad\qquad 3 = C(-3)(-2),$$

from which $A = -2$, $B = \frac{5}{2}$, $C = \frac{1}{2}$.   Therefore

$$\frac{s^2 - 6}{s^3 + 4s^2 + 3s} = \frac{-2}{s} + \frac{\frac{5}{2}}{s + 1} + \frac{\frac{1}{2}}{s + 3}.$$

*See, for example, E. D. Rainville, *Unified Calculus and Analytic Geometry*, New York, Macmillan, 1961, pp. 357-364.

Since $L^{-1}\left\{\dfrac{1}{s}\right\} = 1$ and $L^{-1}\left\{\dfrac{1}{s+a}\right\} = e^{-at}$, we get the desired result,

$$L^{-1}\left\{\frac{s^2 - 6}{s^3 + 4s^2 + 3s}\right\} = -2 + \tfrac{5}{2}e^{-t} + \tfrac{1}{2}e^{-3t}.$$

*Example (b).*   Obtain $L^{-1}\left\{\dfrac{5s^3 - 6s - 3}{s^3(s+1)^2}\right\}$.

Since the denominator contains repeated linear factors, we must assume partial fractions of the form shown:

(3) $$\frac{5s^3 - 6s - 3}{s^3(s+1)^2} = \frac{A_1}{s} + \frac{A_2}{s^2} + \frac{A_3}{s^3} + \frac{B_1}{s+1} + \frac{B_2}{(s+1)^2}.$$

Corresponding to a denominator factor $(x - \gamma)^r$ we must in general, assume $r$ partial fractions of the form

$$\frac{A_1}{x - \gamma} + \frac{A_2}{(x - \gamma)^2} + \cdots + \frac{A_r}{(x - \gamma)^r}.$$

From (3) we get

(4) $\quad 5s^3 - 6s - 3 = A_1s^2(s+1)^2 + A_2s(s+1)^2$
$$+ A_3(s+1)^2 + B_1s^3(s+1) + B_2s^3,$$

which must be an identity in $s$.   To get the necessary five equations for the determination of $A_1$, $A_2$, $A_3$, $B_1$, $B_2$, two elementary methods are popular. Specific values of $s$ can be used in (4), or the coefficients of like powers of $s$ in the two members of (4) may be equated.   We employ whatever combination of these methods yields simple equations to be solved for $A_1$, $A_2$, $\cdots$, $B_2$.   From (4) we obtain

$$
\begin{array}{ll}
s = 0: & -3 = A_3(1), \\
s = -1: & -2 = B_2(-1), \\
\text{coeff. of } s^4: & 0 = A_1 + B_1, \\
\text{coeff. of } s^3: & 5 = 2A_1 + A_2 + B_1 + B_2, \\
\text{coeff. of } s: & -6 = A_2 + 2A_3.
\end{array}
$$

The above equations yield $A_1 = 3$, $A_2 = 0$, $A_3 = -3$, $B_1 = -3$, $B_2 = 2$. Therefore we find that

$$L^{-1}\left\{\frac{5s^3 - 6s - 3}{s^3(s+1)^2}\right\} = L^{-1}\left\{\frac{3}{s} - \frac{3}{s^3} - \frac{3}{s+1} + \frac{2}{(s+1)^2}\right\}$$
$$= 3 - \tfrac{3}{2}t^2 - 3e^{-t} + 2te^{-t}.$$

*Example (c).*   Obtain $L^{-1}\left\{\dfrac{16}{s(s^2 + 4)^2}\right\}$.

Since quadratic factors require the corresponding partial fractions to have linear numerators, we start with an expansion of the form

$$\frac{16}{s(s^2+4)^2} = \frac{A}{s} \quad \frac{B_1 s + C_1}{s^2+4} + \frac{B_2 s + C_2}{(s^2+4)^2}.$$

From the identity

$$16 = A(s^2+4)^2 + (B_1 s + C_1)s(s^2+4) + (B_2 s + C_2)s$$

it is not difficult to find the values $A = 1$, $B_1 = -1$, $B_2 = -4$, $C_1 = 0$, $C_2 = 0$. We thus obtain

$$L^{-1}\left\{\frac{16}{s(s^2+4)^2}\right\} = L^{-1}\left\{\frac{1}{s} - \frac{s}{s^2+4} - \frac{4s}{(s^2+4)^2}\right\}$$

$$= 1 - \cos 2t - t \sin 2t.$$

It is possible to obtain formulas for the partial fractions expansion of the rational fractions being treated in this section. Such formulas are useful in theory and not particularly inefficient in practice. The elementary techniques above, if used intelligently, are efficient in numerical problems and are the only partial fractions methods presented in this short treatment of the subject.

## EXERCISES

In Exs. 1-10, find an inverse transform of the given $f(s)$.

1. $\dfrac{1}{s^2+as}$.                                   *Ans.* $\dfrac{1}{a}(1 - e^{-at})$.

2. $\dfrac{s+2}{s^2-6s+8}$.                                 *Ans.* $3e^{4t} - 2e^{2t}$.

3. $\dfrac{2s^2+5s-4}{s^3+s^2-2s}$.                          *Ans.* $2 + e^t - e^{-2t}$.

4. $\dfrac{2s^2+1}{s(s+1)^2}$.                              *Ans.* $1 + e^{-t} - 3te^{-t}$.

5. $\dfrac{4s+4}{s^2(s-2)}$.                                *Ans.* $3e^{2t} - 3 - 2t$.

6. $\dfrac{1}{s^3(s^2+1)}$.                                 *Ans.* $\frac{1}{2}t^2 - 1 + \cos t$.

7. $\dfrac{5s-2}{s^2(s+2)(s-1)}$.                           *Ans.* $t - 2 + e^t + e^{-2t}$.

8. $\dfrac{1}{(s^2+a^2)(s^2+b^2)}$,     $a^2 \neq b^2$, $ab \neq 0$.     *Ans.* $\dfrac{b \sin at - a \sin bt}{ab(b^2 - a^2)}$.

9. $\dfrac{s}{(s^2+a^2)(s^2+b^2)}$,     $a^2 \neq b^2$,  $ab \neq 0$.    *Ans.* $\dfrac{\cos at - \cos bt}{b^2 - a^2}$.

10. $\dfrac{s^2}{(s^2+a^2)(s^2+b^2)}$,     $a^2 \neq b^2$,  $ab \neq 0$.   *Ans.* $\dfrac{a \sin at - b \sin bt}{a^2 - b^2}$.

11. Obtain the answers to Exs. 9 and 10 from that for Ex. 8.

12. Use equation (8), page 15 and the convolution. Theorem 16, to obtain

$$L^{-1}\left\{\frac{16}{s(s^2+4)^2}\right\} = \int_0^t (\sin 2\beta - 2\beta \cos 2\beta)d\beta,$$

and then perform the integration to check the answer to Example (c), page 32.

## 15. *Simple Boundary Value Problems*

Because of Theorem 6, page 13, the Laplace operator will transform a differential equation with constant coefficients* into an algebraic equation in the transformed function. Several examples will be treated in detail so that we can get some feeling for the advantages and disadvantages of the transform method. One fact is apparent from the start: this method is at its best when the boundary conditions are actually initial conditions, those giving the value of the function and its derivatives at time zero.

*Example* (a). Solve the problem

(1) $$y''(t) + \beta^2 y(t) = A \sin \omega t; \qquad y(0) = 1, \quad y'(0) = 0.$$

Here $A$, $\beta$, $\omega$ are constants. Since $\beta = 0$ would make the problem one of elementary calculus and since a change in sign of $\beta$ or $\omega$ would not alter the character of the problem, we may assume without harm that $\beta$ and $\omega$ are positive.

Let $\qquad\qquad L\{y(t)\} = u(s).$

Then $\qquad\qquad L\{y'(t)\} = su(s) - 1,$
$\qquad\qquad\qquad L\{y''(t)\} = s^2 u(s) - s \cdot 1 - 0,$

and application of the operator $L$ transforms the problem (1) into

$$s^2 u(s) - s + \beta^2 u(s) = \frac{A\omega}{s^2 + \omega^2},$$

from which

(2) $$u(s) = \frac{s}{s^2 + \beta^2} + \frac{A\omega}{(s^2 + \beta^2)(s^2 + \omega^2)}.$$

We need the inverse transform of the right member of (2). The form of that inverse depends upon whether $\beta$ and $\omega$ are equal or unequal.
If $\omega \neq \beta$,

$$u(s) = \frac{s}{s^2 + \beta^2} + \frac{A\omega}{\beta^2 - \omega^2}\left(\frac{1}{s^2 + \omega^2} - \frac{1}{s^2 + \beta^2}\right)$$

$$= \frac{s}{s^2 + \beta^2} + \frac{A}{\beta(\beta^2 - \omega^2)}\left(\frac{\omega\beta}{s^2 + \omega^2} - \frac{\omega\beta}{s^2 + \beta^2}\right).$$

Now $y(t) = L^{-1}\{u(s)\}$ so that, for $\omega \neq \beta$,

(3) $\quad y(t) = \cos \beta t + \dfrac{A}{\beta(\beta^2 - \omega^2)}\,(\beta \sin \omega t - \omega \sin \beta t)\,.$

If $\omega = \beta$, the transform (2) becomes

(4) $$u(s) = \frac{s}{s^2 + \beta^2} + \frac{A\beta}{(s^2 + \beta^2)^2}.$$

*Equations with variable coefficients will be considered briefly in Chapter 5.

We know that

$$L^{-1}\left\{\frac{1}{(s^2 + \beta^2)^2}\right\} = \frac{1}{2\beta^3}\,(\sin \beta t - \beta t \cos \beta t).$$

Hence, for $\omega = \beta$,

(5) $$y(t) = \cos \beta t + \frac{A}{2\beta^2}\,(\sin \beta t - \beta t \cos \beta t).$$

Note that the initial conditions were satisfied automatically by this method when Theorem 6 was applied. We get, not the general solution with arbitrary constants still to be determined, but that particular solution which satisfies the desired initial conditions. The transform method also give us some insight into the reason that the solution takes different forms according to whether $\omega$ and $\beta$ are equal or unequal.

*Example (b).* Solve the problem

(6) $$x''(t) + 2x'(t) + x(t) = 3te^{-t}; \qquad x(0) = 4, \quad x'(0) = 2.$$

Let $L\{x(t)\} = y(s)$. Then the operator $L$ converts (6) into

$$s^2y(s) - 4s - 2 + 2[sy(s) - 4] + y(s) = \frac{3}{(s + 1)^2},$$

or

(7) $$y(s) = \frac{4s + 10}{(s + 1)^2} + \frac{3}{(s + 1)^4}.$$

We may write

$$y(s) = \frac{4(s + 1) + 6}{(s + 1)^2} + \frac{3}{(s + 1)^4}$$

$$= \frac{4}{s + 1} + \frac{6}{(s + 1)^2} + \frac{3}{(s + 1)^4}.$$

Employing the inverse transform we obtain

(8) $$x(t) = (4 + 6t + \tfrac{1}{2}t^3)e^{-t}.$$

Again the presence of initial conditions contributed to the efficiency of our method. In obtaining, and in using, equation (7) those terms which came from the initial values $x(0)$ and $x'(0)$ were not combined with the term which came from the transform of the right member of the differential equation. To combine such terms rarely simplifies and frequently complicates the task of obtaining the inverse transform.

From the solution

(8) $$x(t) = (4 + 6t + \tfrac{1}{2}t^3)e^{-t}$$

the student should obtain the derivatives

$$x'(t) = (2 - 6t + \tfrac{3}{2}t^2 - \tfrac{1}{2}t^3)e^{-t},$$
$$x''(t) = (-8 + 9t - 3t^2 + \tfrac{1}{2}t^3)e^{-t},$$

and thus verify that the $x$ of (8) satisfies both the differential equation and the initial conditions of the problem (6). Such verification not only checks our work but also removes any need to justify temporary assumptions about the right to use the Laplace transform theorems on the function $x(t)$ during the time that function is still unknown.

*Example (c).* Solve the problem

$$(9) \qquad x''(t) + 4x(t) = \psi(t); \qquad x(0) = 1, \qquad x'(0) = 0,$$

in which $\psi(t)$ is defined by

$$
\begin{aligned}
(10) \qquad \psi(t) &= 4t, & 0 \leq t \leq 1, \\
&= 4, & t > 1.
\end{aligned}
$$

We seek, of course, a solution valid in the range $t \geq 0$ in which the right member $\psi(t)$ is defined.

In this problem another phase of the power of the Laplace transform method begins to emerge. The fact that the function $\psi(t)$ in the differential equation has discontinuous derivatives makes the use of the classical method of undetermined coefficients somewhat awkward, but such discontinuities do not interfere at all with the simplicity of the Laplace transform method.

In attacking this problem let us put $L\{x(t)\} = h(s)$. We need to obtain $L\{\psi(t)\}$. In terms of the $\alpha$ function of §12 we may write, from (10),

$$(11) \qquad \psi(t) = 4t - 4(t - 1)\alpha(t - 1), \qquad t \geq 0.$$

From (11) it follows that

$$L\{\psi(t)\} = \frac{4}{s^2} - \frac{4e^{-s}}{s^2}.$$

Therefore the application of the operator $L$ transforms the problem (9) above into

$$s^2 h(s) - s - 0 + 4h(s) = \frac{4}{s^2} - \frac{4e^{-s}}{s^2},$$

from which

$$(12) \qquad h(s) = \frac{s}{s^2 + 4} + \frac{4}{s^2(s^2 + 4)} - \frac{4e^{-s}}{s^2(s^2 + 4)}.$$

Now

$$\frac{4}{s^2(s^2 + 4)} = \frac{1}{s^2} - \frac{1}{s^2 + 4},$$

so that (12) becomes

$$(13) \qquad h(s) = \frac{s}{s^2 + 4} + \frac{1}{s^2} - \frac{1}{s^2 + 4} - \left(\frac{1}{s^2} - \frac{1}{s^2 + 4}\right)e^{-s}.$$

Since $x(t) = L^{-1}\{h(s)\}$, we obtain the desired solution

$$(14) \quad x(t) = \cos 2t + t - \tfrac{1}{2}\sin 2t - [(t - 1) - \tfrac{1}{2}\sin 2(t - 1)]\alpha(t - 1).$$

It is easy to verify our solution.   From (14) it follows that

(15)     $x'(t) = -2 \sin 2t + 1 - \cos 2t - [1 - \cos 2(t - 1)]\alpha(t - 1)$

and

(16)       $x''(t) = -4 \cos 2t + 2 \sin 2t - 2 \sin 2(t - 1)\alpha(t - 1).$

Therefore $x(0) = 1$ and $x'(0) = 0$, as desired.   Also, from (14) – (16), we get

$$x''(t) + 4x(t) = 4t - 4(t - 1)\alpha(t - 1) = \psi(t), \qquad t \geq 0.$$

*Example (d).*   Solve the problem

(17)        $x''(t) + k^2 x(t) = F(t); \qquad x(0) = A, \qquad x'(0) = B.$

Here $k$, $A$, $B$ are constants and $F(t)$ is a known but unstipulated function. For the time being, think of $F(t)$ as a function whose Laplace transform exists.   Let

$$L\{x(t)\} = u(s), \qquad L\{F(t)\} = f(s) .$$

Then the Laplace operator transforms the problem (17) into

$$s^2 u(s) - As - B + k^2 u(s) = f(s) ,$$

or

(18)                    $u(s) = \dfrac{As + B}{s^2 + k^2} + \dfrac{f(s)}{s^2 + k^2}.$

In order to get the inverse transform of the last term in (18), we use the convolution theorem.   Thus we arrive at

$$x(t) = A \cos kt + \frac{B}{k} \sin kt + \frac{1}{k} \int_0^t F(t - \beta) \sin k\beta \, d\beta,$$

or

(19)        $x(t) = A \cos kt + \dfrac{B}{k} \sin kt + \dfrac{1}{k} \int_0^t F(\beta) \sin k(t - \beta) \, d\beta.$

For the student who has had advanced calculus and knows how to differentiate a definite integral with respect to a parameter (Leibniz' rule), verification of the solution (19) is simple.   Once that check has been performed the need for the assumption that $F(t)$ has a Laplace transform is removed.   It does not matter what method we use to get a solution (with certain exceptions naturally imposed during college examinations) if the validity of the result can be verified from the result itself.

*Example (e).*   Solve the problem

(20)     $w''(x) + 2w'(x) + w(x) = x; \qquad w(0) = -3, \qquad w(1) = -1.$

In this example the boundary conditions are not both of the initial condition type.   Using $x$, rather than $t$, as independent variable, let

(21)                        $L\{w(x)\} = g(s) .$

We know $w(0) = -3$, but we also need $w'(0)$ in order to write the transform of $w''(x)$. Hence we put

(22) $$w'(0) = B$$

and expect to determine $B$ later by using the condition that $w(1) = -1$.

The transformed problem is

$$s^2 g(s) - s(-3) - B + 2[sg(s) - (-3)] + g(s) = \frac{1}{s^2}.$$

from which

$$g(s) = \frac{-3s - 6 + B}{(s+1)^2} + \frac{1}{s^2(s+1)^2},$$

(23) $$g(s) = \frac{-3(s+1) + B - 3}{(s+1)^2} + \frac{1}{s^2(s+1)^2}.$$

But, by the usual partial fractions expansion,

$$\frac{1}{s^2(s+1)^2} = -\frac{2}{s} + \frac{1}{s^2} + \frac{2}{s+1} + \frac{1}{(s+1)^2},$$

so that

(24) $$g(s) = \frac{1}{s^2} - \frac{2}{s} - \frac{1}{s+1} + \frac{B-2}{(s+1)^2},$$

from which we obtain

(25) $$w(x) = x - 2 - e^{-x} + (B-2)xe^{-x}.$$

We have yet to impose the condition that $w(1) = -1$. From (25) with $x = 1$, we get

$$-1 = 1 - 2 - e^{-1} + (B-2)e^{-1},$$

so that $B = 3$.

Thus our final result is

(26) $$w(x) = x - 2 - e^{-x} + xe^{-x}.$$

## EXERCISES

In Exs. 1–14, solve the problem by the Laplace transform method. Verify that your solution satisfies the differential equation and the boundary conditions.

**1.** $x''(t) + 4x'(t) + 4x(t) = 4e^{-2t}$; $x(0) = -1$, $x'(0) = 4$.
$$\textit{Ans. } x(t) = e^{-2t}(2t^2 + 2t - 1).$$

**2.** $x''(t) + x(t) = 6 \cos 2t$; $x(0) = 3$, $x'(0) = 1$.
$$\textit{Ans. } x(t) = 5 \cos t + \sin t - 2 \cos 2t.$$

**3.** $y''(t) - y(t) = 5 \sin 2t$; $y(0) = 0$, $y'(0) = 1$. $\quad$ $\textit{Ans. } y(t) = 3 \sinh t - \sin 2t.$

**4.** $y''(t) + 6y'(t) + 9y(t) = 6t^2 e^{-3t}$; $y(0) = 0$, $y'(0) = 0$. $\quad$ $\textit{Ans. } y(t) = \frac{1}{2}t^4 e^{-3t}.$

**5.** $x''(t) + 4x(t) = 2t - 8$; $x(0) = 1$, $x'(0) = 0$.
$$\textit{Ans. } x(t) = 3 \cos 2t - \frac{1}{4} \sin 2t + \frac{1}{2}t - 2.$$

**6.** $x''(t) + 2x'(t) = 8t; x(0) = 0, x'(0) = 0.$          *Ans.* $x(t) = 2t^2 - 2t + 1 - e^{-2t}.$

**7.** $u''(t) + 4u(t) = 15e^t; u(0) = 1, u'(0) = 3.$          *Ans.* $u(t) = 3e^t - 2 \cos 2t.$

**8.** $u''(t) + 4u'(t) + 3u(t) = 12; u(0) = 7, u'(0) = 1.$

$$Ans.\ u(t) = 4 + 5e^{-t} - 2e^{-3t}.$$

**9.** $y''(x) + 9y(x) = 40e^x; y(0) = 5, y'(0) = -2.$

$$Ans.\ y(x) = 4e^x + \cos 3x - 2 \sin 3x.$$

**10.** $y''(x) + y(x) = 4e^x; y(0) = 0, y'(0) = 0.$

$$Ans.\ y(x) = 2(e^x - \cos x - \sin x).$$

**11.** $x''(t) + 3x'(t) + 2x(t) = 4t^2; x(0) = 0, x'(0) = 0.$

$$Ans.\ x(t) = 2t^2 - 6t + 7 - 8e^{-t} + e^{-2t}.$$

**12.** $x''(t) - 4x'(t) + 4x(t) = 4 \cos 2t; x(0) = 2, x'(0) = 5.$

$$Ans.\ x(t) = 2e^{2t}(1 + t) - \tfrac{1}{2} \sin 2t.$$

**13.** $x''(t) + x(t) = F(t); x(0) = 0, x'(0) = 0,$ in which

$$F(t) = 4, \quad 0 \leq t \leq 2,$$
$$= t + 2, \quad t > 2.$$

$$Ans.\ x(t) = 4 - 4 \cos t + [(t - 2) - \sin(t - 2)]\alpha(t - 2) \cdot$$

**14.** $x''(t) + x(t) = H(t); x(0) = 1, x'(0) = 0,$ in which

$$H(t) = 3, \quad 0 \leq t \leq 4,$$
$$= 2t - 5, \quad t > 4.$$

$$Ans.\ x(t) = 3 - 2 \cos t + 2[t - 4 - \sin(t - 4)]\alpha(t - 4) \cdot$$

**15.** Compute $y(\tfrac{1}{2}\pi)$ and $y(2 + \tfrac{1}{2}\pi)$ for the function $y(x)$ which satisfies the boundary value problem

$$y''(x) + y(x) = (x - 2)\alpha(x - 2); y(0) = 0, y'(0) = 0.$$

$$Ans.\ y(\tfrac{1}{2}\pi) = 0, y(2 + \tfrac{1}{2}\pi) = \tfrac{1}{2}\pi - 1.$$

**16.** Compute $x(1)$ and $x(4)$ for the function $x(t)$ which satisfies the boundary value problem

$$x''(t) + 2x'(t) + x(t) = 2 + (t - 3)\alpha(t - 3); x(0) = 2, x'(0) = 1.$$

$$Ans.\ x(1) = 2 + e^{-1}, x(4) = 1 + 3e^{-1} + 4e^{-4}.$$

**17.** Solve the problem

$$x''(t) + 2x'(t) + x(t) = F(t); x(0) = 0, x'(0) = 0.$$

$$Ans.\ x(t) = \int_0^t \beta e^{-\beta} F(t - \beta)d\beta.$$

**18.** Solve the problem

$$y''(t) - k^2 y(t) = H(t); y(0) = 0, y'(0) = 0.$$

$$Ans.\ y(t) = \frac{1}{k} \int_0^t H(t - \beta)\sinh k\beta \, d\beta.$$

**19.** Solve the problem

$$y''(t) + 4y'(t) + 13y(t) = F(t); y(0) = 0, y'(0) = 0.$$

$$Ans.\ y(t) = \frac{1}{3} \int_0^t e^{-2\beta} \sin 3\beta F(t - \beta)d\beta.$$

**20.** Solve the problem

$$x''(t) + 6x'(t) + 9x(t) = F(t); x(0) = A, x'(0) = B.$$

$$Ans.\ x(t) = e^{-3t}[A + (B + 3A)t] + \int_0^t \beta e^{-3\beta} F(t - \beta)d\beta.$$

**21.** Solve the problem
$$x''(t) - 4x'(t) + 4x(t) = e^{2t}; \ x'(0) = 0, \ x(1) = 0.$$

*Ans.* $x(t) = \frac{1}{2}(1 - t)^2 e^{2t}$.

**22.** Solve the problem
$$x''(t) + 4x(t) = -8t^2; \ x(0) = 3, \ x(\tfrac{1}{4}\pi) = 0.$$

*Ans.* $x(t) = 2 \cos 2t + \left(\frac{1}{8}\pi^2 - 1\right) \sin 2t + 1 - 2t^2$.

## 16. *Special Integral Equations*

A differential equation may be loosely described as one which contains a derivative of a dependent variable; the equation contains a dependent variable under a derivative sign. An equation which contains a dependent variable under an integral sign is called an integral equation.

Because of the convolution theorem, the Laplace transform is an excellent tool for solving a very special class of integral equations. We know from Theorem 16 that if

$$L\{F(t)\} = f(s)$$

and

$$L\{G(t)\} = g(s) \, ,$$

then

(1) $$L\left\{\int_0^t F(\beta)G(t - \beta) \, d\beta\right\} = f(s)g(s) \cdot$$

The relation (1) suggests the use of the Laplace transform on equations which contain a convolution integral.

*Example (a).* Find $F(t)$ from the integral equation

(2) $$F(t) = 4t - 3 \int_0^t F(\beta) \sin(t - \beta) \, d\beta \cdot$$

The integral in (2) is in precisely the right form to permit the use of the convolution theorem. Let

$$L\{F(t)\} = f(s) \, .$$

Then, since

$$L\{\sin t\} = \frac{1}{s^2 + 1},$$

application of Theorem 16, page 30, yields

$$L\left\{\int_0^t F(\beta) \sin(t - \beta) \, d\beta\right\} = \frac{f(s)}{s^2 + 1} \cdot$$

Therefore, the Laplace operator converts equation (2) into

(3) $$f(s) = \frac{4}{s^2} - \frac{3f(s)}{s^2 + 1} \cdot$$

We need to obtain $f(s)$ from (3) and then $F(t)$ from $f(s)$. From (3) we get

$$\left(1 + \frac{3}{s^2 + 1}\right) f(s) = \frac{4}{s^2},$$

or

$$f(s) = \frac{4(s^2 + 1)}{s^2(s^2 + 4)}.$$

Then, by the methods of §14, or by inspection,

$$f(s) = \frac{1}{s^2} + \frac{3}{s^2 + 4}.$$

Therefore

$$F(t) = L^{-1}\left\{\frac{1}{s^2} + \frac{3}{s^2 + 4}\right\},$$

or

(4)                                $F(t) = t + \tfrac{3}{2} \sin 2t.$

That the $F(t)$ of (4) is a solution of equation (2) may be verified directly. Such a check is frequently tedious. We shall show that for the $F$ of (4) the righthand side of equation (2) reduces to the lefthand side of (2). Since

$$RHS = 4t - 3 \int_0^t (\beta + \tfrac{3}{2} \sin 2\beta) \sin(t - \beta) \, d\beta,$$

we integrate by parts with the choice shown in the table.

| $(\beta + \tfrac{3}{2} \sin 2\beta)$ | $\sin(t - \beta) \, d\beta$ |
| --- | --- |
| $(1 + 3 \cos 2\beta) \, d\beta$ | $\cos (t - \beta)$ |

It thus follows that

$$RHS = 4t - 3\left[ (\beta + \tfrac{3}{2} \sin 2\beta) \cos(t - \beta) \right]_0^t$$

$$+ 3 \int_0^t (1 + 3 \cos 2\beta) \cos(t - \beta) \, d\beta,$$

from which

$$RHS = 4t - 3(t + \tfrac{3}{2} \sin 2t) + 3 \int_0^t \cos(t - \beta) \, d\beta$$

$$+ 9 \int_0^t \cos 2\beta \cos(t - \beta) \, d\beta,$$

or

$$RHS = t - \tfrac{9}{2} \sin 2t - 3\left[ \sin(t - \beta) \right]_0^t + \tfrac{9}{2} \int_0^t [\cos(t + \beta) + \cos(t - 3\beta)] \, d\beta.$$

This leads us to the result

$$RHS = t - \tfrac{9}{2}\sin 2t + 3\sin t + \tfrac{9}{2}\left[\sin(t+\beta) - \tfrac{1}{3}\sin(t-3\beta)\right]_0^t$$

$$= t - \tfrac{9}{2}\sin 2t + 3\sin t + \tfrac{9}{2}\sin 2t + \tfrac{3}{2}\sin 2t - \tfrac{9}{2}\sin t + \tfrac{3}{2}\sin t,$$

or

$$RHS = t + \tfrac{3}{2}\sin 2t = F(t) = LHS,$$

as desired.

It is important to realize that the original equation

$$(2) \qquad\qquad F(t) = 4t - 3\int_0^t F(\beta)\sin(t-\beta)\,d\beta$$

could equally well have been encountered in the equivalent form

$$F(t) = 4t - 3\int_0^t F(t-\beta)\sin\beta\,d\beta.$$

An essential ingredient for the success of the method being used is that the integral involved be in exactly the convolution integral form. We must have zero to the independent variable as limits of integration and an integrand which is the product of a function of the variable of integration by a function of the difference between the independent variable and the variable of integration. The fact that integrals of that form appear with some frequency in physical problems is all that keeps the topic of this section from being relegated to the role of a mathematical parlor game.

*Example (b).* Solve the equation

$$(5) \qquad\qquad g(x) = \tfrac{1}{2}x^2 - \int_0^x (x-y)g(y)\,dy.$$

Again the integral involved is one of the convolution type with $x$ playing the role of the independent variable. Let the Laplace transform of $g(x)$ be some, as yet unknown, function $h(z)$:

$$(6) \qquad\qquad L\{g(x)\} = h(z).$$

Since $L\{\tfrac{1}{2}x^2\} = \dfrac{1}{z^3}$ and $L\{x\} = \dfrac{1}{z^2}$, we may apply the operator $L$ throughout (5) and obtain

$$h(z) = \frac{1}{z^3} - \frac{h(z)}{z^2},$$

from which

$$\left(1 + \frac{1}{z^2}\right)h(z) = \frac{1}{z^3},$$

or

$$h(z) = \frac{1}{z(z^2+1)} = \frac{z^2+1-z^2}{z(z^2+1)} = \frac{1}{z} - \frac{z}{z^2+1}.$$

Then
$$g(x) = L^{-1}\left\{\frac{1}{z} - \frac{z}{z^2 + 1}\right\}$$

or

(7)                         $g(x) = 1 - \cos x.$

Verification of (7) is simple.   For the right member of (5) we get

$$RHS = \tfrac{1}{2}x^2 - \int_0^x (x - y)(1 - \cos y)\, dy$$

$$= \tfrac{1}{2}x^2 - \left[(x - y)(y - \sin y)\right]_0^x - \int_0^x (y - \sin y)\, dy$$

$$= \tfrac{1}{2}x^2 - 0 - \left[\tfrac{1}{2}y^2 + \cos y\right]_0^x$$

$$= \tfrac{1}{2}x^2 - \tfrac{1}{2}x^2 - \cos x + 1 = 1 - \cos x = LHS.$$

## EXERCISES

In Exs. 1–4, solve the given equation and verify your solution.

**1.** $F(t) = 1 + 2\int_0^t F(t - \beta)e^{-2\beta}d\beta.$      *Ans.* $F(t) = 1 + 2t.$

**2.** $F(t) = 1 + \int_0^t F(\beta) \sin(t - \beta)d\beta.$      *Ans.* $F(t) = 1 + \tfrac{1}{2}t^2.$

**3.** $F(t) = t + \int_0^t F(t - \beta)e^{-\beta}d\beta.$      *Ans.* $F(t) = t + \tfrac{1}{2}t^2.$

**4.** $F(t) = 4t^2 - \int_0^t F(t - \beta)e^{-\beta}d\beta.$      *Ans.* $F(t) = -1 + 2t + 2t^2 + e^{-2t}.$

In Exs. 5–8, solve the given equation.   If sufficient time is available, verify your solution.

**5.** $F(t) = t^3 + \int_0^t F(\beta) \sin(t - \beta)\, d\beta.$      *Ans.* $F(t) = t^3 + \dfrac{1}{20}t^5.$

**6.** $F(t) = 8t^2 - 3\int_0^t F(\beta) \sin(t - \beta)\, d\beta.$      *Ans.* $F(t) = 2t^2 + 3 - 3 \cos 2t.$

**7.** $F(t) = t^2 - 2\int_0^t F(t - \beta) \sinh 2\beta\, d\beta.$      *Ans.* $F(t) = t^2 - \dfrac{1}{3}t^4.$

**8.** $F(t) = 1 + 2\int_0^t F(t - \beta) \cos \beta\, d\beta.$      *Ans.* $F(t) = 1 + 2te^t.$

In Exs. 9–12, solve the given equation.

**9.** $H(t) = 9e^{2t} - 2\int_0^t H(t - \beta) \cos \beta\, d\beta.$      *Ans.* $H(t) = 5e^{2t} + 4e^{-t} - 6te^{-t}.$

**10.** $H(y) = y^2 + \int_0^y H(x) \sin(y - x) \, dx.$        *Ans.* $H(y) = y^2 + \dfrac{1}{12} y^4.$

**11.** $g(x) = e^{-x} - 2 \int_0^x g(\beta) \cos(x - \beta) \, d\beta.$        *Ans.* $g(x) = e^{-x}(1 - x)^2.$

**12.** $y(t) = 6t + 4 \int_0^t (\beta - t)^2 y(\beta) \, d\beta.$

*Ans.* $y(t) = e^{2t} - e^{-t} (\cos\sqrt{3}\, t - \sqrt{3} \sin\sqrt{3}\, t).$

**13.** Solve the following equation for $F(t)$ with the condition that $F(0) = 4$:

$$F'(t) = t + \int_0^t F(t - \beta) \cos \beta \, d\beta.$$        *Ans.* $F(t) = 4 + \dfrac{5}{2} t^2 + \dfrac{1}{24} t^4.$

**14.** Solve the following equation for $F(t)$ with the condition that $F(0) = 0$:

$$F'(t) = \sin t + \int_0^t F(t - \beta) \cos \beta \, d\beta.$$        *Ans.* $F(t) = \tfrac{1}{2}t^2.$

**15.** Show that the equation of Ex. 3 above can be put in the form

(A)        $$e^t F(t) = te^t + \int_0^t e^\beta F(\beta) \, d\beta.$$

Differentiate each member of (A) with respect to $t$ and thus replace the integral equation by a differential equation. Note that $F(0) = 0$. Find $F(t)$ by this method.

**16.** Solve the equation

$$\int_0^t F(t - \beta) e^{-\beta} \, d\beta = t$$

by two methods; use the convolution theorem and the basic idea introduced in Ex. 15. Note that no differential equation need be solved in this instance.

$$3$$

# Applications

## 17. *Vibration of a Spring*

Consider a steel spring attached to a support and hanging downward. Within certain elastic limits the spring will obey Hooke's law: if the spring is stretched or compressed, its change in length will be proportional to the force exerted upon the spring and, when that force is removed, the spring will return to its original position with its length and other physical properties unchanged. There is, therefore, associated with each spring a numerical constant, the ratio of the force exerted to the displacement produced by that force. If a force of magnitude $Q$ pounds stretches the spring $l$ feet, the relation

(1)     $$Q = kl$$

defines the spring constant $k$ in the units pounds per foot.

Let a body $B$ weighing $w$ pounds be attached to the lower end of the spring (Fig. 12) and brought to the point of equilibrium where it can remain at rest. Once the weight $B$ is moved from the point of equilibrium $E$ in Fig. 13, the

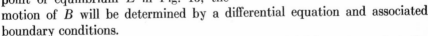

Fig. 12          Fig. 13

motion of $B$ will be determined by a differential equation and associated boundary conditions.

Let $t$ be time measured in seconds after some initial moment when the motion begins. Let $x$, in feet, be distance measured positive downward (negative upward) from the point of equilibrium, as in Fig. 13. We assume that the motion of $B$ takes place entirely in a vertical line so that the velocity and acceleration are given by the first and second derivatives of $x$ with respect to $t$.

In addition to the force proportional to displacement (Hooke's law) there will in general be a retarding force caused by resistance of the medium in which the motion takes place or by friction.   We are interested here in only such retarding forces as can be well approximated by a term proportional to the velocity because we restrict our study to problems involving linear differential equations.   Such a retarding force will contribute to the total force acting on $B$ a term $bx'(t)$, in which $b$ is a constant to be determined experimentally for the medium in which the motion takes place.   Some common retarding forces, such as one proportional to the cube of the velocity, lead to nonlinear differential equations which are not amenable to treatment by the Laplace transform.

The weight of the spring is usually negligible compared to the weight $B$, so we use for the mass of our system the weight of $B$ divided by $g$, the constant acceleration of gravity.   If no forces other than those described above act upon the weight, the displacement $x$ must satisfy the equation

$$(2) \qquad \frac{w}{g} x''(t) + bx'(t) + kx(t) = 0.$$

Suppose an additional vertical force, due to the motion of the support or to presence of a magnetic field, etc., is imposed upon the system.   The new, impressed force, will depend upon time and we may use $F(t)$ to denote the acceleration which it alone would impart to the weight $B$.   Then the impressed force is $\dfrac{w}{g} F(t)$ and differential equation (2) is replaced by

$$(3) \qquad \frac{w}{g} x''(t) + bx'(t) + kx(t) = \frac{w}{g} F(t) .$$

We may, of course, include (2) in (3) by using $F(t) \equiv 0$.

At time zero let the weight be displaced by an amount $x_0$ from the equilibrium point and let the weight be given an initial velocity $v_0$.   Either or both of $x_0$ and $v_0$ may be zero in specific instances.   The problem of determining the position of the weight at any time $t$ becomes that of solving the boundary value problem consisting of the differential equation

$$(4) \qquad \frac{w}{g} x''(t) + bx'(t) + kx(t) = \frac{w}{g} F(t), \qquad \text{for } t > 0,$$

and the initial conditions

$$(5) \qquad\qquad x(0) = x_0 , \qquad x'(0) = v_0 .$$

It is convenient to rewrite equation (4) in the form

$$(6) \qquad\qquad x''(t) + 2\gamma x'(t) + \beta^2 x(t) = F(t) .$$

in which we have put

$$\frac{bg}{w} = 2\gamma, \qquad \frac{kg}{w} = \beta^2.$$

We may choose $\beta > 0$ and we know $\gamma \geqq 0$.   Note that $\gamma = 0$ corresponds to a negligible retarding force.

Impressed forces so illbehaved that their Laplace transforms do not exist are hardly worth considering. We therefore let

(7) $$L\{x(t)\} = u(s), \quad L\{F(t)\} = f(s),$$

and obtain from the problem (5) and (6) the transformed problem

$$s^2u(s) - sx_0 - v_0 + 2\gamma[su(s) - x_0] + \beta^2u(s) = f(s),$$

$$u(s) = \frac{sx_0 + v_0 + 2\gamma x_0}{s^2 + 2\gamma s + \beta^2} + \frac{f(s)}{s^2 + 2\gamma s + \beta^2},$$

which we write as

(8) $$u(s) = \frac{x_0(s + \gamma) + v_0 + \gamma x_0}{(s + \gamma)^2 + \beta^2 - \gamma^2} + \frac{f(s)}{(s + \gamma)^2 + \beta^2 - \gamma^2}.$$

The desired $x(t)$ is the inverse transform of $u(s)$.

Here we begin to reap benefits from our use of the Laplace transform. Even before we get $x(t)$ we can see that its form will depend upon whether the denominator in (8) has distinct real linear factors, equal factors, or is the sum of two squares. That is, the form of $x(t)$ will depend upon whether $\beta < \gamma$, $\beta = \gamma$, or $\beta > \gamma$. Furthermore, if $\gamma \neq 0$, we can predict the presence of a damping factor $e^{-\gamma t}$ in $x(t)$.

The inverse of the $u(s)$ of equation (8) can be obtained with our standard methods, including the convolution theorem. When the $F(t)$ is reasonably simple, one of the types which occur frequently in practice, the convolution theorem leads to forms less desirable than those obtained by the other methods in Chapter 2.

We shall now consider separately the various situations which arise according to the choice of parameters $\beta$ and $\gamma$ and the forcing function $F(t)$ in this problem of the vibrating spring.

In treating spring problems we are particularly interested in impressed forces which lead to $F(t)$ of forms such as those listed:

(a) No impressed force: $F(t) = 0$;

(b) Simple harmonic forcing function:

$$F(t) = A_1 \sin \omega t + A_2 \cos \omega t;$$

(c) Temporary constant force:

$$F(t) = A, \quad 0 < t < t_0,$$
$$= 0, \qquad t > t_0;$$

(d) A delayed form of (c):

$$F(t) = 0, \quad 0 < t < t_0,$$
$$= A, \quad t_0 < t < t_1,$$
$$= 0, \qquad t > t_1;$$

(e) $F(t) =$ the half-wave rectification of a sine curve.

It will become apparent when we study electric circuits in §22 that all of our present work carries over to simple circuit problems with new meanings attached to the parameters and functions involved. In circuit theory we shall add to the forms of $F(t)$ listed above both $F(t)$ equal to a constant and an $F(t)$ equal to the square wave function which appeared in §10.

## 18. *Undamped Vibrations*

If $\gamma = 0$ in the spring problem of §17, the transform $u(s)$ becomes

$$(1) \qquad u(s) = \frac{x_0 s + v_0}{s^2 + \beta^2} + \frac{f(s)}{s^2 + \beta^2}.$$

The inverse transform of the first term on the right in (1) is

$$x_0 \cos \beta t + \frac{v_0}{\beta} \sin \beta t,$$

which contributes to $x(t)$ a simple harmonic motion, called the *natural component* of the motion, natural because it is independent of the forcing function $F(t)$. From the last term in (1) we obtain the forced component, the form of which is dependent upon $F(t)$.

Instead of jumping from (1) to the general solution

$$(2) \qquad x(t) = x_0 \cos \beta t + v_0 \beta^{-1} \sin \beta t + \beta^{-1} \int_0^t F(t - v) \sin \beta v \, dv,$$

we prefer to obtain $x(t)$ without a convolution integral for the specific types of $F(t)$ which occur often. Equation (2) was easily obtained but it leaves all the labor of simplification to the unfortunate user who has a particular $F(t)$ with which to deal.

*Example (a).* Solve the spring problem with no damping but with a forcing function $F(t) = A \sin \omega t$.

The differential equation of motion is

$$\frac{w}{g} x''(t) + kx(t) = \frac{w}{g} A \sin \omega t$$

and is readily put into the form

$$(3) \qquad x''(t) + \beta^2 x(t) = A \sin \omega t$$

with the introduction of $\beta^2 = kg/w$. We shall assume initial conditions

$$(4) \qquad x(0) = x_0, \quad x'(0) = v_0.$$

Let $L\{x(t)\} = u(s)$. Then (3) and (4) yield

$$s^2 u(s) - sx_0 - v_0 + \beta^2 u(s) = \frac{A\omega}{s^2 + \omega^2},$$

or

$$(5) \qquad u(s) = \frac{sx_0 + v_0}{s^2 + \beta^2} + \frac{A\omega}{(s^2 + \beta^2)(s^2 + \omega^2)}.$$

The last term in (5) will lead to different inverse transforms according to whether $\omega = \beta$ or $\omega \neq \beta$. The case $\omega = \beta$ leads to resonance, which will be discussed in the next section.

If $\omega \neq \beta$, equation (5) yields

$$(6) \qquad u(s) = \frac{sx_0 + v_0}{s^2 + \beta^2} + \frac{A\omega}{\omega^2 - \beta^2}\left(\frac{1}{s^2 + \beta^2} - \frac{1}{s^2 + \omega^2}\right).$$

From (6) it follows at once that

$$(7) \quad x(t) = x_0 \cos \beta t + v_0\beta^{-1} \sin \beta t + \frac{A\omega}{\beta(\omega^2 - \beta^2)} \sin \beta t - \frac{A}{\omega^2 - \beta^2} \sin \omega t.$$

That the $x$ of (7) is a solution of the problem (3) and (4) is easily verified. A study of (7) is simple and leads at once to conclusions such as that $x(t)$ is bounded, etc. The first two terms on the right in (7) yield the natural harmonic component of the motion, the last two terms form the forced component.

*Example (b).* A spring is such that it would be stretched 6 inches by a 12-pound weight. Let the weight be attached to the spring and pulled down 4 inches below the equilibrium point. If the weight is started with an upward velocity of 2 feet per second, describe the motion. No damping or impressed force is present.

We know that the acceleration of gravity enters our work in the expression for the mass. We wish to use the value $g = 32$ ft. per sec. per sec. and we must use consistent units, so we put all lengths into feet.

First we determine the spring constant $k$ from the fact that the 12-pound weight stretches the spring 6 inches, $\frac{1}{2}$ ft. Thus $12 = \frac{1}{2}k$ so that $k = 24$ lb. per ft.

The differential equation of the motion is therefore

$$(8) \qquad \frac{12}{32} x''(t) + 24x(t) = 0.$$

At time zero the weight is 4 inches ($\frac{1}{3}$ ft.) below the equilibrium point, so $x(0) = \frac{1}{3}$. The initial velocity is negative (upward), so $x'(0) = -2$. Thus our problem is that of solving

$$(9) \qquad x''(t) + 64x(t) = 0; \qquad x(0) = \tfrac{1}{3}, \quad x'(0) = -2.$$

We let $L\{x(t)\} = u(s)$ and conclude at once that

$$s^2u(s) - \tfrac{1}{3} s + 2 + 64u(s) = 0,$$

from which

$$u(s) = \frac{\frac{1}{3}s - 2}{s^2 + 64}.$$

Then

(10) $$x(t) = \tfrac{1}{3} \cos 8t - \tfrac{1}{4} \sin 8t.$$

A detailed discussion of the motion is straightforward once (10) has been obtained. The amplitude of the motion is

$$\sqrt{(\tfrac{1}{3})^2 + (\tfrac{1}{4})^2} = \tfrac{5}{12} \; ;$$

that is, the weight oscillates between points 5 inches above and below $E$. The period is $\tfrac{1}{4}\pi$ sec.

*Example* (c). A spring, with spring constant 0.75 lb. per ft., lies on a long smooth (frictionless) table. A 6-lb. weight is attached to the spring and is at rest (velocity zero) at the equilibrium position. A 1.5-lb. force is applied to the support along the line of action of the spring for 4 seconds and is then removed. Discuss the motion.

We must solve the problem

(11) $$\tfrac{6}{32} x''(t) + \tfrac{3}{4} x(t) = H(t); \qquad x(0) = 0, \quad x'(0) = 0,$$

in which

$$H(t) = 1.5, \qquad 0 < t < 4,$$
$$= 0, \qquad\qquad t > 4.$$

Now $H(t) = 1.5[1 - \alpha(t - 4)]$ in terms of the $\alpha$ function of §12. Therefore we rewrite our problem (11) in the form

(12) $$x''(t) + 4x(t) = 8[1 - \alpha(t - 4)]; \quad x(0) = 0, \quad x'(0) = 0.$$

Let $L\{x(t)\} = u(s)$. Then (12) yields

$$s^2 u(s) + 4u(s) = \frac{8}{s} (1 - e^{-4s}) ,$$

or

$$u(s) = \frac{8(1 - e^{-4s})}{s(s^2 + 4)}$$

$$= 2 \left( \frac{1}{s} - \frac{s}{s^2 + 4} \right) (1 - e^{-4s}) .$$

The desired solution is

(13) $$x(t) = 2(1 - \cos 2t) - 2[1 - \cos 2(t - 4)]\alpha(t - 4) .$$

Of course, the solution (13) can be broken down into the two relations

(14) For $0 \leq t \leq 4$, $\quad x(t) = 2(1 - \cos 2t)$,

(15) For $t > 4$, $\quad x(t) = 2[\cos 2(t - 4) - \cos 2t]$ ,

if those forms seem simpler to use.

Verification of the solution (13), or (14) and (15), is direct.   The student should show that

$$\operatorname*{Lim}_{t\to 4^-} x(t) = \operatorname*{Lim}_{t\to 4^+} x(t) = 2(1 - \cos 8) = 2.29$$

and

$$\operatorname*{Lim}_{t\to 4^-} x'(t) = \operatorname*{Lim}_{t\to 4^+} x'(t) = 4 \sin 8 = 3.96.$$

From (13) or (14) we see that in the range $0 < t < 4$, the maximum deviation of the weight from the starting point is $x = 4$ ft. and occurs at $t = \frac{1}{2}\pi = 1.57$ sec.   At $t = 4$, $x = 2.29$ ft. as shown above.   For $t > 4$ equation (15) takes over and thereafter the motion is simple harmonic with a maximum $x$ of 3.03 ft.   Indeed, for $t > 4$,

$$\max |x(t)| = 2\sqrt{(1 - \cos 8)^2 + \sin^2 8}$$

$$= 2\sqrt{2}\,\sqrt{1 - \cos 8}$$

$$= 2\sqrt{2.2910} = 3.03.$$

Example (c) is one type of problem for which the Laplace transform technique is particularly useful.   Such problems can be solved by the older classical methods, but with much less simplicity and dispatch.

## 19. *Resonance*

In the problem of undamped vibrations of a spring one of the examples we encountered was

(1)        $x''(t) + \beta^2 x(t) = A \sin \omega t;$     $x(0) = x_0,$   $x'(0) = v_0.$

The solution of (1) was obtained by putting $L\{x(t)\} = u(s)$ and getting

(2)          $u(s) = \dfrac{sx_0 + v_0}{s^2 + \beta^2} + \dfrac{A\omega}{(s^2 + \beta^2)(s^2 + \omega^2)}.$

From (2) we see that the inverse transform differs according to whether $\omega = \beta$ or $\omega \neq \beta$.   The latter situation has been studied.   Let us now assume $\omega = \beta$.

Our problem is to solve

(3)        $x''(t) + \beta^2 x(t) = A \sin \beta t;$     $x(0) = x_0,$   $x'(0) = v_0$

with the aid of

(4)          $u(s) = \dfrac{sx_0 + v_0}{s^2 + \beta^2} + \dfrac{A\beta}{(s^2 + \beta^2)^2}.$

We already know, page 15, that

$$L^{-1}\left\{\frac{1}{(s^2 + \beta^2)^2}\right\} = \frac{1}{2\beta^3}(\sin \beta t - \beta t \cos \beta t).$$

Therefore (4) leads us to the solution

$$(5) \qquad x(t) = x_0 \cos \beta t + \frac{v_0}{\beta} \sin \beta t + \frac{A}{2\beta^2} (\sin \beta t - \beta t \cos \beta t).$$

That (5) satisfies all the conditions of (3) is readily verified.

In the solution (5) the terms proportional to $\cos \beta t$ and $\sin \beta t$ are bounded, but the term with $\beta t \cos \beta t$ can be made as large as we wish by proper choice of $t$. This building up of large amplitudes in the vibration when $\omega = \beta$ in (1) is called *resonance*. We shall see later that damping ($\gamma \neq 0$ in §17) prevents resonance from occurring.

## 20. *Damped Vibrations*

In the general linear spring problem of §17 we were confronted with

$$(1) \qquad x''(t) + 2\gamma x'(t) + \beta^2 x(t) = F(t); \qquad x(0) = x_0, \quad x'(0) = v_0,$$

in which $\gamma = \dfrac{bg}{w}$ and $\beta^2 = \dfrac{kg}{w}$, $\beta > 0$. We let

$$L\{x(t)\} = u(s), \qquad L\{F(t)\} = f(s)$$

and obtained

$$(2) \qquad u(s) = \frac{x_0(s + \gamma) + v_0 + \gamma x_0}{(s + \gamma)^2 + \beta^2 - \gamma^2} + \frac{f(s)}{(s + \gamma)^2 + \beta^2 - \gamma^2}.$$

We are now concerned with $\gamma > 0$; a nonnegligible retarding force is present. We know that the form of the inverse transform of $u(s)$ depends upon whether $\beta > \gamma$, $\beta = \gamma$, or $\beta < \gamma$.

If $\beta > \gamma$, $\beta^2 - \gamma^2 > 0$, so let us put

$$(3) \qquad\qquad\qquad \beta^2 - \gamma^2 = \delta^2.$$

Then (2) becomes

$$(4) \qquad\qquad u(s) = \frac{x_0(s + \gamma) + v_0 + \gamma x_0}{(s + \gamma)^2 + \delta^2} + \frac{f(s)}{(s + \gamma)^2 + \delta^2}$$

and we arrive at

$$(5) \qquad x(t) = e^{-\gamma t} [x_0 \cos \delta t + (v_0 + \gamma x_0)\delta^{-1} \sin \delta t] + \psi_1(t)$$

in which $\psi_1(t)$ is an inverse transform of the last term in (4). The function $\psi_1(t)$ can always be written in terms of $F(t)$ by the convolution theorem but that leads to undesirable complications for the most common choices of $F(t)$. In the solution (5) the presence of the damping factor $e^{-\gamma t}$ shows that the natural component of the motion approaches zero as $t \to \infty$.

If in (1) and (2) we have $\beta = \gamma$, the transform

$$(6) \qquad\qquad u(s) = \frac{x_0(s + \gamma) + v_0 + \gamma x_0}{(s + \gamma)^2} + \frac{f(s)}{(s + \gamma)^2}$$

leads us to the solution

(7) $$x(t) = e^{-\gamma t}\left[x_0 + (v_0 + \gamma x_0)t\right] + \psi_2(t),$$

in which $\psi_2(t)$ is an inverse of $(s + \gamma)^{-2}f(s)$ and is easily determined once $F(t)$ is stipulated. Again the natural component has the damping factor $e^{-\gamma t}$ in it.

If in (1) and (2) we have $\beta < \gamma$, $\gamma^2 - \beta^2 > 0$ and we put

(8) $$\gamma^2 - \beta^2 = \sigma^2.$$

Then (2) becomes

(9) $$u(s) = \frac{x_0(s + \gamma) + v_0 + \gamma x_0}{(s + \gamma)^2 - \sigma^2} + \frac{f(s)}{(s + \gamma)^2 - \sigma^2}$$

which leads to the solution

(10) $$x(t) = e^{-\gamma t}[x_0 \cosh \sigma t + (v_0 + \gamma x_0)\sigma^{-1} \sinh \sigma t] + \psi_3(t),$$

in which $\psi_3(t)$ is an inverse of the last term in (9). By (8) we see that $\gamma > \sigma$, so that once more the natural component of the $x(t)$ in (10) approaches zero as $t \to \infty$.

Suppose for the moment that we have $F(t) \equiv 0$, so that the natural component of the motion is all that is under consideration. If $\beta > \gamma$, equation (5) holds and the motion is a damped oscillatory one. If $\beta = \gamma$, equation (7) holds and the motion is not oscillatory; it is called *critically damped* motion. If $\beta < \gamma$, (10) holds and the motion is said to be *overdamped;* the parameter $\gamma$ is larger than it needs to be to remove the oscillations. Figure 14 shows a representative graph of each type of motion mentioned in this

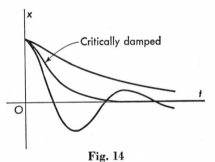

Fig. 14

paragraph, a damped oscillatory motion, a critically damped one, and an overdamped one.

## EXERCISES

**1.** A spring is such that a 5-pound weight stretches it 6 inches. The 5-pound weight is attached, the spring reaches equilibrium, then the weight is pulled down 3 inches below the equilibrium point and started off with an upward velocity of 6 ft. per sec. Find an equation giving the position of the weight at all subsequent times.

*Ans.* $x = \frac{1}{4}(\cos 8t - 3 \sin 8t)$.

**2.** A spring is stretched 1.5 inches by a 2-pound weight. Let the weight be pushed up 3 inches above $E$ and then released. Describe the motion.

*Ans.* $x = -\frac{1}{4} \cos 16t$.

**3.** For the spring and weight of Ex. 2 let the weight be pulled down 4 inches below $E$ and given a downward initial velocity of 8 ft. per sec. Describe the motion.

*Ans.* $x = \frac{1}{3} \cos 16t + \frac{1}{2} \sin 16t$.

**4.** A 20-pound weight stretches a certain spring 10 inches. Let the spring first be compressed 4 inches, and then the 20-pound weight attached and given an initial downward velocity of 8 ft. per sec. Find how far the weight would drop.

*Ans.* 35 in.

**5.** A spring is such that a 4-pound weight stretches it 0.64 feet. The 4-pound weight is pushed up $\frac{1}{3}$ foot above the point of equilibrium and then started with a downward velocity of 5 ft. per sec. The motion takes place in a medium which furnishes a damping force of magnitude $\frac{1}{4}|v|$ at all times. Find the equation describing the position of the weight at time $t$. *Ans.* $x = \frac{1}{3}e^{-t}(2 \sin 7t - \cos 7t)$.

**6.** A spring is such that a 4-pound weight stretches it 0.32 feet. The weight is attached to the spring and moves in a medium which furnishes a damping force of magnitude $\frac{3}{2}|v|$. The weight is drawn down $\frac{1}{2}$ foot below the equilibrium point and given an initial upward velocity of 4 ft. per sec. Find the position of the weight thereafter. *Ans.* $x = \frac{1}{8}e^{-6t}(4 \cos 8t - \sin 8t)$.

**7.** A spring is such that a 4-pound weight stretches the spring 0.4 feet. The 4-pound weight is attached to the spring (suspended from a fixed support) and the system is allowed to reach equilibrium. Then the weight is started from equilibrium position with an imparted upward velocity of 2 ft. per sec. Assume that the motion takes place in a medium which furnishes a retarding force of magnitude numerically equal to the speed, in feet per second, of the moving weight. Determine the position of the weight as a function of time. *Ans.* $x = -\frac{1}{4}e^{-4t} \sin 8t$.

**8.** A spring is stretched 6 inches by a 3-pound weight. The 3-pound weight is attached to the spring and then started from equilibrium with an imparted upward velocity of 12 ft. per sec. Air resistance furnishes a retarding force equal in magnitude to $0.03|v|$. Find the equation of motion of the weight.

*Ans.* $x = -1.5e^{-0.16t} \sin 8t$.

**9.** A spring is such that a 4-pound weight stretches it 6 inches. There is no appreciable damping present, but an impressed force $\frac{1}{2} \cos 8t$ is acting on the spring. If the 4-pound weight is started from the equilibrium point with an imparted upward velocity of 4 ft. per sec, determine the position of the weight as a function of time.

*Ans.* $x = \frac{1}{4}(t - 2) \sin 8t$.

**10.** A spring is such that a 2-pound weight stretches it $\frac{1}{2}$ foot. An impressed force $\frac{1}{4} \sin 8t$ and a damping force of magnitude $|v|$ are both acting on the spring. The weight starts $\frac{1}{4}$ foot below the equilibrium point with an imparted upward velocity of 3 ft. per sec. Find a formula for the position of the weight at time $t$.

*Ans.* $x = \frac{3}{32}e^{-8t}(3 - 8t) - \frac{1}{32} \cos 8t$.

**11.** A spring is such that a 16-pound weight stretches it 1.5 inches. The weight is pulled down to a point 4 inches below the equilibrium point and given an initial downward velocity of 4 ft. per sec. There is no damping force present, but there is an impressed force of $360 \cos 4t$ pounds. Find the position and velocity of the weight at time $t = \pi/8$ seconds.

*Ans.* At $t = \pi/8$(sec). $x = -\frac{8}{3}$ (ft.), $v = -8$ (ft./sec).

**12.** A spring is such that a 4-pound weight stretches it 6 inches. The 4-pound weight is attached to the vertical spring and reaches its equilibrium point. The weight is then $(t = 0)$ drawn downward 3 inches and released. No damping force is present, but there is a simple harmonic exterior force equal to sin $8t$ impressed upon the whole system. Find the time for each of the first 4 stops following $t = 0$. Put the stops in chronological order.          *Ans.* $t = \pi/8, \frac{1}{2}, \pi/4, 3\pi/8$ (sec).

**13.** A spring is such that a 2-pound weight stretches it 6 inches. There is a damping force present, with magnitude the same as the magnitude of the velocity. An impressed force $(2 \sin 8t)$ is acting on the spring. If, at $t = 0$, the weight is released from a point 3 inches below the equilibrium point, find its position for $t > 0$.
*Ans.* $x = (\frac{1}{2} + 4t)e^{-8t} - \frac{1}{4} \cos 8t$.

**14.** A spring is such that a 2-pound weight stretches it $\frac{1}{2}$ foot. An impressed force $\frac{1}{4} \sin 8t$ is acting upon the spring. If the 2-pound weight is released from a point 3 inches below the equilibrium point, determine the equation of motion.
*Ans.* $x = \frac{1}{4}(1 - t) \cos 8t + \frac{1}{32} \sin 8t$ (ft.).

**15.** Let the motion of Ex. 14 be retarded by a damping force of magnitude $|v|$. Find the equation of motion and also determine its form (to the nearest 0.01 ft.) for $t > 1$ (sec).
*Ans.* $x = \frac{9}{32}(8t + 1)e^{-8t} - \frac{1}{32} \cos 8t$ (ft.); for $t > 1$, $x = -\frac{1}{32} \cos 8t$.

**16.** Let the motion of Ex. 14 be retarded by a damping force of magnitude $\frac{5}{3}|v|$. Find the equation of motion.          *Ans.* $x = 0.30e^{-(8/3)t} - 0.03e^{-24t} - 0.02 \cos 8t$.

**17.** A spring is stretched 6 inches by a 4-pound weight. Let the weight be pulled down 6 inches below equilibrium and given an initial upward velocity of 7 ft. per sec. Assuming a damping force twice the magnitude of the velocity, describe the motion and sketch the graph for $0 \leq t \leq 0.3$ (sec) at intervals of 0.05 sec.
*Ans.* $x = \frac{1}{2}e^{-8t}(1 - 6t)$.

**18.** A spring is stretched 1.5 inches by a 4-pound weight. Let the weight be pulled down 3 inches below equilibrium and released. If there is an impressed force $8 \sin 16t$ acting upon the spring, but no damping force is present, describe the motion.
*Ans.* $x = \frac{1}{4}(1 - 8t) \cos 16t + \frac{1}{8} \sin 16t$.

**19.** An object weighing $w$ pounds is dropped from a height $h$ feet above the earth. At time $t$ (sec) after the object is dropped let its distance from the starting point be $x$ (ft.), measured positive downward. Assuming air resistance to be negligible, show that $x$ must satisfy the equation

$$\frac{w}{g} \frac{d^2x}{dt^2} = w$$

as long as $x < h$. Find $x$.          *Ans.* $x = \frac{1}{2}gt^2$.

**20.** Let the weight of Ex. 19 be given an initial velocity $v_0$. Let $v$ be the velocity at time $t$. Determine $v$ and $x$.          *Ans.* $v = gt + v_0$, $x = \frac{1}{2}gt^2 + v_0t$.

**21.** From the results in Ex. 20 find a relation which does not contain $t$ explicitly.
*Ans.* $v^2 = v_0^2 + 2gx$.

**22.** If air resistance furnishes an additional force proportional to the velocity in the motion studied in Ex. 19 and 20 above show that the equation of motion becomes

(A)          $$\frac{w}{g} \frac{d^2x}{dt^2} + b \frac{dx}{dt} = w.$$

Solve equation (A) together with the conditions

(B)          when $t = 0$, $x = 0$ and $v = v_0$.

Use $a = bg/w$.          *Ans.* $x = a^{-1}gt + a^{-2}(av_0 - g)(1 - e^{-at})$.

**23.** In order to compare the results of Ex. 20 and Ex. 22 when $a = bg/w$ is small, use the power series for $e^{-at}$ in the answer for Ex. 22 and discard all terms involving $a^n$ for $n \geq 3$.     *Ans.* $x = \frac{1}{2}gt^2 + v_0 t - \frac{1}{6}at^2(3v_0 + gt) + \frac{1}{24}a^2t^3(4v_0 + gt)$.

**24.** The equation of motion of the vertical fall of a man with a parachute may be roughly approximated by equation (A) of Ex. 22. Suppose a 180-pound man drops from a great height and attains a velocity of 20 miles per hour after a long time. Determine the implied coefficient $b$ of equation (A).     *Ans.* 6.1 (lb.) (sec) per (ft.).

**25.** A particle is moving along the $x$-axis according to the law

$$\frac{d^2x}{dt^2} + 6\frac{dx}{dt} + 25x = 0.$$

If the particle started at $x = 0$ with an initial velocity of 12 (ft. per sec) to the left, determine: (a) $x$ in terms of $t$, (b) the times at which stops occur, and (c) the ratio between the numerical values of $x$ at successive stops.

*Ans.* (a) $x = -3e^{-3t}\sin 4t$,

(b) $t = 0.23 + n\pi/4$, $n = 0, 1, 2, 3, \ldots$, (c) 0.095.

## 21. *The Simple Pendulum*

A rod of length $C$ feet is suspended by one end so that it can swing freely in a vertical plane. Let a weight $B$ (the bob) of $w$ pounds be attached to the free end of the rod, and let the weight of the rod be negligible compared to the weight of the bob.

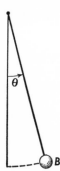

Let $\theta$ (radians) be the angular displacement from the vertical, as shown in Figure 15, of the rod at time $t$ (sec). The tangential component of the force $w$ (lb.) is $w \sin \theta$ and it tends to decrease $\theta$. Then, neglecting the weight of the rod and using $s = C\theta$ as a measure of arc length from the vertical position, we may conclude that

(1)     $$\frac{w}{g}\frac{d^2s}{dt^2} = -w \sin \theta.$$

Since $s = C\theta$ and $C$ is constant, (1) becomes

**Fig. 15**     (2)     $$\frac{d^2\theta}{dt^2} + \frac{g}{C}\sin \theta = 0.$$

The solution of equation (2) is not elementary; it involves an elliptic integral. If $\theta$ is small, however, $\sin \theta$ and $\theta$ are nearly equal and (2) is closely approximated by the much simpler equation

(3)     $$\frac{d^2\theta}{dt^2} + \beta^2\theta = 0; \quad \beta^2 = g/C.$$

The solution of (3) with pertinent boundary conditions gives usable results whenever those conditions are such that $\theta$ remains small, say $|\theta| < 0.3$ (radians). Recall also that in the derivation it was assumed that the effect of the weight of the rod is negligible compared to that of the weight of the bob.

**EXERCISES**

1. A clock has a 6-inch pendulum. The clock ticks once for each time that the pendulum completes a swing, returning to its original position. How many times does the clock tick in 30 seconds? *Ans.* 38 times.

2. A 6-inch pendulum is released from rest at an angle one-tenth of a radian from the vertical. Using $g = 32$ (ft. per sec per sec), describe the motion.
*Ans.* $\theta = 0.1 \cos 8t$ (radians).

3. For the pendulum of Ex. 2 find the maximum angular speed and its first time of occurrence. *Ans.* 0.8 (rad per sec) at 0.2 sec.

4. A 6-inch pendulum is started with a velocity of one radian per second, toward the vertical, from a position one-tenth radian from the vertical. Describe the motion. *Ans.* $\theta = \frac{1}{10} \cos 8t - \frac{1}{8} \sin 8t$ (radians).

5. For Ex. 4 find to the nearest degree the maximum angular displacement from the vertical. *Ans.* 9°.

6. Interpret as a pendulum problem and solve the boundary value problem:

(A) $$\frac{d^2\theta}{dt^2} + \beta^2\theta = 0; \; \beta^2 = g/C,$$

(B) $$\text{when } t = 0, \; \theta = \theta_0 \text{ and } \omega = \frac{d\theta}{dt} = \omega_0 .$$

*Ans.* $\theta = \theta_0 \cos \beta t + \beta^{-1}\omega_0 \sin \beta t$ (radians).

7. Find the maximum angular displacement from the vertical for the pendulum of Ex. 6. *Ans.* $\theta_{\max} = (\theta_0{}^2 + \beta^{-2}\omega_0{}^2)^{1/2}$.

## 22. *Electric Circuits*

The basic laws which govern the flow of electric current in a circuit or a network will be given here without derivation. The notation used is common to most texts in electrical engineering; it is:

$t$  (sec) = time
$Q$  (coulombs) = quantity of electricity; e.g., charge on a capacitor
$I$  (amperes) = current, time rate of flow of electricity
$E$  (volts) = electromotive force or voltage
$R$  (ohms) = resistance
$L$  (henrys) = inductance
$C$  (farads) = capacitance.

By the definition of $Q$ and $I$ it follows that

$$I(t) = Q'(t) .$$

The current at each point in a network may be determined by solving the equations which result from applying Kirchhoff's laws:

(a) *The sum of the currents into (or away from) any point is zero,*

and

(b) *Around any closed path the sum of the instantaneous voltage drops in a specified direction is zero.*

A circuit is treated as a network containing only one closed path. Figure 16 exhibits an "*RLC* circuit" with some of the customary conventions for indicating various elements.

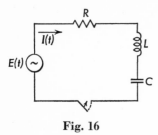

**Fig. 16**

For a circuit Kirchhoff's current law (a) indicates merely that the current is the same throughout. That law plays a larger role in networks, as we shall see later.

In order to apply Kirchhoff's voltage law (b) it is necessary to have the contributions of each of the idealized elements in Fig. 16. The voltage drop across the resistance is $RI$, that across the inductance is $LI'(t)$, while the capacitor contributes $C^{-1}Q(t)$. The impressed electromotive force $E(t)$ is contributing a voltage rise.

Assume that at time $t = 0$ the switch shown in Fig. 16 is to be closed. At $t = 0$ there is no current flowing, $I(0) = 0$, and if the capacitor is initially without charge, $Q(0) = 0$. From Kirchhoff's law (b) we get the differential equation

$$(1) \qquad LI'(t) + RI(t) + C^{-1}Q(t) = E(t),$$

in which

$$(2) \qquad I(t) = Q'(t).$$

Equations (1) and (2) together with the initial conditions

$$(3) \qquad I(0) = 0, \qquad Q(0) = 0,$$

constitute the problem to be solved.

In order to retain the conventional symbol $L$ for the number of henrys inductance of the circuit, we shall in this section denote by $L_t$ the Laplace operator for which $L$ is used in all other sections of the book.

Let the Laplace transforms of $I(t)$, $Q(t)$, $E(t)$ be denoted by lower case letters:

$$(4) \qquad L_t\{I(t)\} = i(s), \qquad L_t\{Q(t)\} = q(s), \qquad L_t\{E(t)\} = e(s).$$

The problem (1) − (3) is then transformed into

$$(5) \qquad L\, si(s) + Ri(s) + C^{-1}q(s) = e(s),$$

$$(6) \qquad i(s) = sq(s).$$

From (5) and (6) we find either or both of $i(s)$ and $q(s)$,

$$(7) \qquad i(s) = \frac{se(s)}{Ls^2 + Rs + C^{-1}},$$

$$(8) \qquad q(s) = \frac{e(s)}{Ls^2 + Rs + C^{-1}}.$$

Then $I(t)$ and $Q(t)$ are obtained as inverse transforms from (7) and (8) once $E(t)$ is specified and the character of the real factors of the quadratic denominator is known.

From (7), (8), or the differential equation

$$(9) \qquad LQ''(t) + RQ'(t) + C^{-1}Q(t) = E(t),$$

it follows that the circuit problem is equivalent to a problem in damped vibrations of a spring, §20. The resistance term $RQ'(t)$ parallels the damping term in vibration problems. The analogies between electrical and mechanical systems are useful in practice.

*Example.* In the $RL$ circuit with the schematic diagram shown in Fig. 17, let the switch be closed at $t = 0$. At some later time, $t = t_0$, the direct current element, the constant $E$, is to be removed from the circuit, which remains closed. Find the current for all $t > 0$.

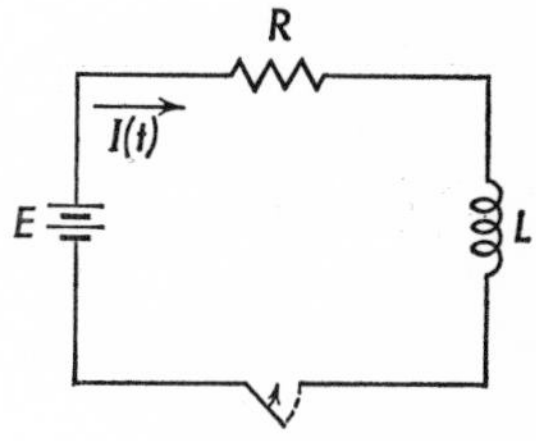

The boundary value problem to be solved is

$$(10) \qquad LI'(t) + RI(t) = E(t); \quad I(0) = 0,$$

$$(11) \qquad E(t) = E[1 - \alpha(t - t_0)].$$

Fig. 17

Let the transform of $I(t)$ be $i(s)$. We know the transform of $E(t)$. Therefore we obtain the transformed problem,

$$(12) \qquad sL\, i(s) + Ri(s) = \frac{E}{s}[1 - \exp(-t_0 s)],$$

from which

$$(13) \qquad i(s) = \frac{E[1 - \exp(-t_0 s)]}{s(sL + R)}.$$

Now

$$\frac{1}{s(sL + R)} = \frac{1}{R}\left(\frac{1}{s} - \frac{1}{s + RL^{-1}}\right),$$

so that

$$i(s) = \frac{E}{R}\left(\frac{1}{s} - \frac{1}{s + RL^{-1}}\right)[1 - \exp(-t_0 s)].$$

Therefore

$$(14)\ I(t) = \frac{E}{R}\left[1 - \alpha(t - t_0) - \exp\left(-\frac{R}{L}t\right) + \exp\left\{-\frac{R}{L}(t - t_0)\right\}\alpha(t - t_0)\right].$$

The student should verify (14) and also show that it can be broken down into the two formulas

$$(15) \qquad \text{For } 0 \leqq t \leqq t_0, \qquad I(t) = \frac{E}{R}\left[1 - \exp\left(-\frac{Rt}{L}\right)\right];$$

(16) For $t > t_0$, $I(t) = I(t_0) \exp\left[-\frac{R}{L}(t - t_0)\right]$.

### EXERCISES

**1.** For the $RL$ circuit of Fig. 17, find the current $I$ if the direct current element $E$ is not removed from the circuit. *Ans.* $I = ER^{-1}[1 - \exp(RtL^{-1})]$.

**2.** Solve Ex. 1 if the direct current element is replaced by an alternating-current element $E \cos \omega t$. For convenience, use the notation $Z^2 = R^2 + \omega^2 L^2$, in which $Z$ is called the steady-state impedance of this circuit.

$$Ans.\ I = EZ^{-2}[\omega L \sin \omega t + R \cos \omega t - R \exp(-RtL^{-1})].$$

**3.** Solve Ex. 2, replacing $E \cos \omega t$ by $E \sin \omega t$.

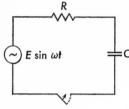

**Fig. 18**

**4.** Figure 18 shows an $RC$ circuit with an alternating-current element inserted. Assume that the switch is closed at $t = 0$ at which time $Q = 0$ and $I = 0$. Use the notation $Z^2 = R^2 + (\omega C)^{-2}$, where $Z$ is the steady-state impedance of this circuit. Find $I$ for $t > 0$.

$$Ans.\ I = EZ^{-2}[R \sin \omega t + (\omega C)^{-1} \cos \omega t - (\omega C)^{-1} \exp(-tR^{-1}C^{-1})].$$

**5.** In Figure 18 replace the alternating-current element with a direct-current element $E = 50$ volts and use $R = 10$ ohms, $C = 4(10)^{-4}$ farad. Assume that when the switch is closed (at $t = 0$) the charge on the capacitor is 0.015 coulomb. Find the initial current in the circuit and the current for $t > 0$.

$$Ans.\ I(0) = 1.25(amp),\ I(t) = 1.25 \exp(-250t).$$

**6.** In Fig. 16, page 58, find $I(t)$ if $E(t) = 60$ volts, $R = 40$ ohms, $C = 5(10)^{-5}$ farad, $L = 0.02$ henry. Assume $I(0) = 0$, $Q(0) = 0$.

$$Ans.\ I = 3000t \exp(-1000t).$$

**7.** In Ex. 6, find the maximum current. *Ans.* $I_{max} = 3e^{-1}(amps)$.

In Exs. 8–11, use Fig. 16 with $E(t) = E \sin \omega t$ and with the following notations used to simplify the appearance of the formulas:

$$a = \frac{R}{2L},\ b^2 = a^2 - \frac{1}{LC},\ \beta^2 = \frac{1}{LC} - a^2,$$

$$\gamma = \omega L - \frac{1}{\omega C},\ Z^2 = R^2 + \gamma^2.$$

The quantity $Z$ is the steady-state impedance for an $RLC$ circuit. In each exercise, find $I(t)$ assuming that $I(0) = 0$ and $Q(0) = 0$.

**8.** Assume that $4L < R^2C$.
$$Ans.\ I = EZ^{-2}(R \sin \omega t - \gamma \cos \omega t) + \tfrac{1}{2}Eb^{-1}Z^{-2}[\{\gamma(a + b) - \omega R\}\exp\{-(a - b)t\} + \{\omega R - \gamma(a - b)\}\exp\{-(a + b)t\}].$$

**9.** Assume that $R^2C < 4L$.
$$Ans.\ I = EZ^{-2}(R \sin \omega t - \gamma \cos \omega t) + E\beta^{-1}Z^{-2}e^{-at}[\beta\gamma \cos \beta t - a(\gamma + 2\omega^{-1}C^{-1}) \sin \beta t].$$

**10.** Assume that $R^2C = 4L$.
$$Ans.\ I = EZ^{-2}(R \sin \omega t - \gamma \cos \omega t) + E\omega^{-1}Z^{-2}e^{-at}[\gamma\omega - a(\gamma\omega + aR)t].$$

**11.** Show that the answer to Ex. 10 can be put in the form
$$I = EZ^{-2}(R \sin \omega t - \gamma \cos \omega t) + EZ^{-2}e^{-at}[\gamma + (a\gamma - R\omega)t].$$

**12.** In Ex. 4 above, replace the alternating current element $E \sin \omega t$ by

$$E[\alpha(t - t_0) - \alpha(t - t_1)], \quad t_1 > t_0 > 0.$$

Graph the new emf. Determine the current in the circuit.

$$Ans. \quad I(t) = \frac{E}{R}\left[ \exp\left(-\frac{t - t_0}{RC}\right) \alpha(t - t_0) - \exp\left(-\frac{t - t_1}{RC}\right) \alpha(t - t_1) \right].$$

## 23. *Beams*

Consider a beam of length $2c$, as shown in Fig. 19. Denote distance from one end of the beam by $x$, the deflection of the beam by $y$. If the beam is subjected to a vertical load $W(x)$, the deflection $y$ must satisfy the equation

$$(1) \qquad\qquad EI\frac{d^4y}{dx^4} = W(x), \qquad \text{for } 0 < x < 2c,$$

in which $E$, the modulus of elasticity and $I$, a moment of inertia, are known constants associated with the particular beam.

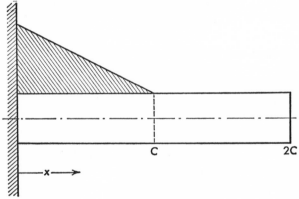

**Fig. 19**

The slope of the curve of deflection is $y'(x)$, the bending moment is $EIy''(x)$, and the shearing force is $EIy'''(x)$. Common boundary conditions are of the following types:

(a) Beam imbedded in a support: $y = 0$ and $y' = 0$ at the point;
(b) Beam simply supported: $y = 0$ and $y'' = 0$ at the point;
(c) Beam free: $y'' = 0$ and $y''' = 0$ at the point.

Problems in the transverse displacement of a beam take the form of the differential equation (1) together with boundary conditions at each end of the beam. Such problems can be solved by integration with the use of a little algebra. There are however two reasons for employing our transform method in such problems. Frequently the load function, or its derivative, is discontinuous. Beam problems also give us a chance to examine a useful device in which a problem over a finite range is solved with the aid of an associated problem over an infinite range.

*Example.* Find the displacement $y$ throughout the beam of Fig. 19 in which the load is assumed to decrease uniformly from $w_0$ at $x = 0$ to zero at $x = c$ and to remain zero from $x = c$ to $x = 2c$. The weight of the beam is to be negligible. The beam is imbedded at $x = 0$ and free at $x = 2c$.

We are to solve the problem

$$(2) \qquad EI\frac{d^4y}{dx^4} = \frac{w_0}{c}[c - x + (x - c)\alpha(x - c)], \qquad \text{for } 0 < x < 2c;$$

$$(3) \qquad\qquad y(0) = 0, \qquad y'(0) = 0;$$

$$(4) \qquad\qquad y''(2c) = 0, \qquad y'''(2c) = 0.$$

The student should verify that the right member of (2) is the stipulated load function

$$(5) \qquad\qquad W(x) = \frac{w_0}{c}(c - x), \qquad \text{for } 0 \leqq x \leqq c,$$

$$= 0, \qquad\qquad \text{for } c < x \leqq 2c.$$

In order to apply the transform technique, with $x$ playing the role for which we usually employ $t$, we need first to extend the range of $x$ so that it will run from 0 to $\infty$. That is, instead of the problem (2), (3), (4) we shall solve the problem consisting of

$$(6) \qquad\qquad EI\frac{d^4y}{dx^4} = H(x), \qquad \text{for } 0 < x < \infty,$$

together with the conditions (3) and (4). In (6) the function $H(x)$ is to be chosen by us except that $H(x)$ must agree with $W(x)$ over the range $0 < x < 2c$. The solution of the problem (6), (3), (4) will then be used only in the range $0 \leqq x \leqq 2c$. Of the various choices for $H(x)$ it seems simplest to use

$$(7) \qquad H(x) = \frac{w_0}{c}[c - x + (x - c)\alpha(x - c)], \qquad \text{for } 0 < x < \infty.$$

That is, in practice we ordinarily retain the equation (2) and merely extend the range from $0 < x < 2c$ to $0 < x < \infty$. The student must, however, keep in mind that we cannot apply the Laplace operator to the function $W(x)$ of (5), since that function is not defined over the entire range, $0 < x < \infty$. We shall solve (6) and conclude that the solution is valid for (2) on the range, $0 \leqq x \leqq 2c$, over which (2) and (6) are identical.

Let $\qquad\qquad L\{EIy(x)\} = u(s); \qquad$ i.e.,

$$(8) \qquad\qquad u(s) = EI\int_0^\infty e^{-sx}y(x)\,dx.$$

In order to transform $EIy^{(4)}(x)$ we need to use the values of $EIy(x)$ and its first three derivatives at $x = 0$. By (3) we know that $EIy(0) = 0$, $EIy'(0) = 0$. Put

(9)                $EIy''(0) = A, \qquad EIy'''(0) = B.$

The constants $A$ and $B$ must be determined by using the conditions (4).
By our usual methods we obtain, for the $H(x)$ of (7),

$$L\{H(x)\} = \frac{w_0}{c} L\{c - x + (x - c)\alpha(x - c)\}$$

$$= \frac{w_0}{c}\left(\frac{c}{s} - \frac{1}{s^2} + \frac{e^{-cs}}{s^2}\right).$$

Thus the differential equation (6) is transformed into

$$s^4 u(s) - s^3 \cdot 0 - s^2 \cdot 0 - s \cdot A - B = \frac{w_0}{c}\left(\frac{c}{s} - \frac{1}{s^2} + \frac{e^{-cs}}{s^2}\right),$$

from which we get

(10)            $$u(s) = \frac{A}{s^3} + \frac{B}{s^4} + \frac{w_0}{c}\left(\frac{c}{s^5} - \frac{1}{s^6} + \frac{e^{-cs}}{s^6}\right).$$

Now $L^{-1}\{u(s)\} = EIy(x)$. Hence

(11)   $EIy(x) = \frac{1}{2}Ax^2 + \frac{1}{6}Bx^3 + \frac{w_0}{120c}\left[5cx^4 - x^5 + (x - c)^5\alpha(x - c)\right].$

From (11) we obtain

(12)   $EIy'(x) = Ax + \frac{1}{2}Bx^2 + \frac{w_0}{24c}\left[4cx^3 - x^4 + (x - 4)^4\alpha(x - c)\right],$

(13)   $EIy''(x) = A + Bx + \frac{w_0}{6c}\left[3cx^2 - x^3 + (x - c)^3\alpha(x - c)\right],$

(14)   $EIy'''(x) = B + \frac{w_0}{2c}\left[2cx - x^2 + (x - c)^2\alpha(x - c)\right].$

By differentiating both members of equation (14) we can see that the $y$
of (11) is a solution of (6) over the infinite range and, more important, a
solution of (2) over the range $0 < x < 2c$.

With the aid of equations (11)–(14) we may now determine $A$ and $B$ to
make the $y$ satisfy appropriate conditions at $x = 2c$, whether the beam be
free, imbedded, or pin supported there. In our example the beam is to be
free at $x = 2c$; the solution is to satisfy the conditions

(4)                $y''(2c) = 0, \qquad y'''(2c) = 0.$

Using (13) and (14), and a little work, we find that (4) requires $A = \frac{1}{6}w_0c^2$,
$B = -\frac{1}{2}w_0c$. We are thus led to the solution

(15)   $EIy(x) = \frac{1}{12}w_0c^2x^2 - \frac{1}{12}w_0cx^3 + \frac{w_0}{120c}\left[5cx^4 - x^5 + (x - c)^5\alpha(x - c)\right],$

for $0 \leqq x \leqq 2c$.

The student should verify by differentiations and appropriate substitutions that the $y$ of (15) satisfies the original differential equation (2) and boundary conditions (3) and (4).

From (15) we may obtain whatever information we wish. For example, at $x = \frac{1}{2}c$ the bending moment is

$$EIy''(\tfrac{1}{2}c) = w_0c^2[\tfrac{1}{6} - \tfrac{1}{4} + \tfrac{1}{6}(-\tfrac{1}{8} + \tfrac{3}{4} + 0)] = \tfrac{1}{48}\,w_0c^2.$$

## EXERCISES

In each exercise find the $y$ which satisfies equation (1), page 61, with the given load function $W(x)$, and the given conditions at the ends of the beam. See (a), (b), (c), page 61. Verify your solutions.

**1.** $W(x)$ as in the above example; beam imbedded at both $x = 0$ and $x = 2c$.

*Ans.* $EIy(x) = \frac{23}{480}w_0c^2x^2 - \frac{3}{40}w_0cx^3 + \dfrac{w_0}{120c}\left[5cx^4 - x^5 + (x - c)^5\alpha(x - c)\right].$

**2.** $W(x) = 0,$     for $0 < x < \frac{1}{2}c,$
         $= w_0,$     for $\frac{1}{2}c < x < \frac{3}{2}c,$
         $= 0,$      for $\frac{3}{2}c < x < 2c;$
beam imbedded at $x = 0$, free at $x = 2c$.

     *Ans.* $EIy(x) = \frac{1}{2}w_0c^2x^2 - \frac{1}{6}w_0cx^3$
                 $+ \frac{1}{24}w_0[(x - \frac{1}{2}c)^4\alpha(x - \frac{1}{2}c) - (x - \frac{3}{2}c)^4\alpha(x - \frac{3}{2}c)].$

**3.** $W(x) = w_0[1 - \alpha(x - c)]$; describe the load. Beam to be imbedded at $x = 0$ and pin-supported (simply supported) at $x = 2c$.

         *Ans.* $EIy(x) = \frac{9}{64}w_0c^2x^2 - \frac{19}{128}w_0cx^3 + \frac{1}{24}w_0[x^4 - (x - c)^4\alpha(x - c)].$

**4.** $W(x) = \dfrac{w_0}{c}(2c - x),$    for $0 < x < c,$

           $= w_0,$   for $c < x < 2c;$

beam to be imbedded at $x = 0$ and free at $x = 2c$.

     *Ans.* $EIy(x) = \frac{13}{12}w_0c^2x^2 - \frac{5}{12}w_0cx^3 + \frac{1}{24}w_0x^4$
                 $+ \dfrac{w_0}{120c}\left[5cx^4 - x^5 + (x - c)^5\alpha(x - c)\right].$

# Systems of Differential Equations

## 24. *Simple Systems*

The Laplace operator can be used to transform a system of linear differential equations with constant coefficients into a system of algebraic equations.

*Example.* Solve the system of equations

(1)  $$x''(t) - x(t) + 5y'(t) = t,$$

(2)  $$y''(t) - 4y(t) - 2x'(t) = -2,$$

with the initial conditions

(3)  $$x(0) = 0, \quad x'(0) = 0, \quad y(0) = 0, \quad y'(0) = 0.$$

Let $L\{x(t)\} = u(s)$ and $L\{y(t)\} = v(s)$. Then application of the Laplace operator transforms the problem above into that of solving a pair of simultaneous algebraic equations:

(4)  $$(s^2 - 1)u(s) + 5sv(s) = \frac{1}{s^2},$$

(5)  $$-2su(s) + (s^2 - 4)v(s) = -\frac{2}{s}.$$

We solve equations (4) and (5) to obtain

(6)  $$u(s) = \frac{11s^2 - 4}{s^2(s^2 + 1)(s^2 + 4)},$$

(7)  $$v(s) = \frac{-2s^2 + 4}{s(s^2 + 1)(s^2 + 4)}.$$

Seeking the inverse transforms of $u$ and $v$, we first expand the right members of (6) and (7) into partial fractions:

(8)
$$u(s) = -\frac{1}{s^2} + \frac{5}{s^2+1} - \frac{4}{s^2+4},$$

(9)
$$v(s) = \frac{1}{s} - \frac{2s}{s^2+1} + \frac{s}{s^2+4}.$$

Since $x(t) = L^{-1}\{u(s)\}$ and $y(t) = L^{-1}\{v(s)\}$, we get the desired results

(10)
$$x(t) = -t + 5 \sin t - 2 \sin 2t,$$

(11)
$$y(t) = 1 - 2 \cos t + \cos 2t,$$

which are easily verified by direct substitution into (1), (2), and (3).

The above procedure is simple in concept and powerful in theoretical studies, but of only moderate efficiency for numerical problems. The student should not overlook the, sometimes tedious, algebra used in passing from (6) and (7) to (8) and (9). The example was deliberately constructed to make the work simple.

## 25. Electric Networks

Systems of differential equations occur naturally in the application of Kirchhoff's laws, page 57, to electric networks. The use of the Laplace operator makes the solution of such systems a straightforward, though often laborious, process. For the general theory of networks the Laplace operator (or its Heaviside equivalent) is a tool of great value. We restrict ourselves to extremely simple situations which should be sufficient to indicate the procedure commonly used.

*Example* (a). Determine the character of the current $I_1(t)$ in the network with the schematic diagram in Fig. 20 under the assumption that when the switch is closed the currents are each zero.

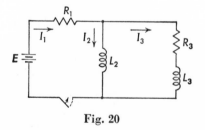

Fig. 20

In a network we apply both of Kirchhoff's laws, page 57, to a system of equations to determine the currents. Since there are three dependent variables present, $I_1$, $I_2$, $I_3$, we need three equations.

From the current law it follows that

(1)
$$I_1 = I_2 + I_3.$$

Application of the voltage law to the circuit on the left in Fig. 20 yields

$$(2) \qquad R_1 I_1 + L_2 \frac{dI_2}{dt} = E.$$

Using the voltage law on the outside circuit, we get

$$(3) \qquad R_1 I_1 + R_3 I_3 + L_3 \frac{dI_3}{dt} = E.$$

Still another equation may be obtained from the circuit on the right in Fig. 20:

$$(4) \qquad R_3 I_3 + L_3 \frac{dI_3}{dt} - L_2 \frac{dI_2}{dt} = 0.$$

Equation (4) also follows at once from equations (2) and (3); it may be used instead of either (2) or (3).

We wish to obtain $I_1(t)$ from the boundary value problem consisting of equations (1), (2), (3), and the conditions $I_1(0) = 0$, $I_2(0) = 0$, $I_3(0) = 0$. One of the three initial conditions is redundant because of equation (1).

Let $L\{I_k(t)\} = i_k(s)$ for each of $k = 1, 2, 3$. Then use of the operator $L$ transforms our problem into the algebraic one of solving the equations

$$(5) \qquad i_1 - i_2 - i_3 = 0,$$

$$(6) \qquad R_1 i_1 + s L_2 i_2 = \frac{E}{s}$$

$$(7) \qquad R_1 i_1 + (R_3 + s L_3) i_3 = \frac{E}{s}.$$

Since we desire only $i_1(s)$, let us use determinants to write the solution

$$(8) \qquad i_1(s) = \frac{\begin{vmatrix} 0 & -1 & -1 \\ \dfrac{E}{s} & sL_2 & 0 \\ \dfrac{E}{s} & 0 & (R_3 + sL_3) \end{vmatrix}}{\Delta} = \frac{E}{s} \cdot \frac{R_3 + s(L_2 + L_3)}{\Delta},$$

in which

$$\Delta = \begin{vmatrix} 1 & -1 & -1 \\ R_1 & sL_2 & 0 \\ R_1 & 0 & (R_3 + sL_3) \end{vmatrix} = \begin{vmatrix} 1 & 0 & 0 \\ R_1 & (sL_2 + R_1) & R_1 \\ R_1 & R_1 & (R_1 + R_3 + sL_3) \end{vmatrix}.$$

Then

$$(9) \qquad \Delta = L_2 L_3 s^2 + (R_1 L_2 + R_3 L_2 + R_1 L_3)s + R_1 R_3.$$

We are interested in the factors of $\Delta$. Consider the equation

(10) $$\Delta = 0.$$

Equation (10) has no positive roots. Its discriminant

$$(R_1L_2 + R_3L_2 + R_1L_3)^2 - 4L_2L_3R_1R_3$$

may be written

$$(R_1L_2)^2 + 2R_1L_2(R_3L_2 + R_1L_3) + (R_3L_2 + R_1L_3)^2 - 4L_2L_3R_1R_3$$

which equals

$$(R_1L_2)^2 + 2R_1L_2(R_3L_2 + R_1L_3) + (R_3L_2 - R_1L_3)^2$$

and is therefore positive. Equation (10) has two distinct negative roots; call them $(-a_1)$ and $(-a_2)$.

Then

$$\Delta = L_2L_3 (s + a_1) (s + a_2)$$

and we have, from (8),

(11) $$\dot{i}_1(s) = \frac{E}{s} \frac{R_3 + s(L_2 + L_3)}{L_2L_3(s + a_1)(s + a_2)}.$$

The right member of equation (11) has a partial fractions expansion

(12) $$\dot{i}_1(s) = \frac{A_0}{s} + \frac{A_1}{s + a_1} + \frac{A_2}{s + a_2}$$

so that

$$I_1(t) = A_0 + A_1 \exp(-a_1t) + A_2 \exp(-a_2t).$$

*Example* (*b*). For the network shown in Fig. 21 set up the equations for the determination of the currents $I_1$, $I_2$, $I_3$ and the charge $Q_3$. Assume that when the switch is closed all currents and charges are zero. Obtain the transformed problem.

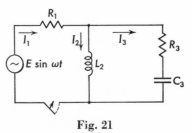

Fig. 21

Using Kirchhoff's laws we write the equations

(13) $$I_1 = I_2 + I_3,$$

$$(14) \qquad R_1 I_1 + L_2 \frac{dI_2}{dt} = E \sin \omega t,$$

$$(15) \qquad R_1 I_1 + R_3 I_3 + \frac{1}{C_3} Q_3 = E \sin \omega t$$

and the definition of current as time rate of change of charge yields

$$(16) \qquad I_3 = \frac{dQ_3}{dt}.$$

Our problem consists of the four equations (13)–(16) with the initial conditions

$$(17) \qquad I_2(0) = 0, \qquad I_3(0) = 0, \qquad Q_3(0) = 0.$$

Let $L\{I_k(t)\} = i_k(s)$, $k = 1, 2, 3$, and let $L\{Q_3(t)\} = q_3(s)$. Then the transformed problem is that of solving the algebraic system

$$(18) \qquad i_1 - i_2 - i_3 = 0,$$

$$(19) \qquad R_1 i_1 + s L_2 i_2 = \frac{E\omega}{s^2 + \omega^2},$$

$$(20) \qquad R_1 i_1 + R_3 i_3 + \frac{1}{C_3} q_3 = \frac{E\omega}{s^2 + \omega^2},$$

$$(21) \qquad i_3 = s q_3 \,.$$

## EXERCISES

In Exs. 1–8, solve the given boundary value problem.

1. $x''(t) - 3x'(t) - y'(t) + 2y(t) = 14t + 3$,
   $x'(t) - 3x(t) + y'(t) = 1$; $x(0) = 0$, $x'(0) = 0$, $y(0) = 6.5$.
   
   Ans. $x(t) = 2 - \frac{1}{2}e^t - \frac{1}{2}e^{3t} - e^{-2t}$,
   $y(t) = 7t + 5 - e^t + \frac{5}{2}e^{-2t}$.

2. $2x'(t) + 2x(t) + y'(t) - y(t) = 3t$,
   $x'(t) + x(t) + y'(t) + y(t) = 1$; $x(0) = 1$, $y(0) = 3$.
   
   Ans. $x(t) = t + 3e^{-t} - 2e^{-3t}$,
   $y(t) = 1 - t + 2e^{-3t}$.

3. $x'(t) - 2x(t) - y'(t) - y(t) = 6e^{3t}$,
   $2x'(t) - 3x(t) + y'(t) - 3y(t) = 6e^{3t}$; $x(0) = 3$, $y(0) = 0$.
   
   Ans. $x(t) = (1 + 2t)e^t + 2e^{3t}$,
   $y(t) = (1 - t)e^t - e^{3t}$.

4. $x''(t) + 2x(t) - y'(t) = 2t + 5$,
   $x'(t) - x(t) + y'(t) + y(t) = -2t - 1$; $x(0) = 3$, $x'(0) = 0$, $y(0) = -3$.
   
   Ans. $x(t) = t + 2 + e^{-2t} + \sin t$,
   $y(t) = 1 - t - 3e^{-2t} - \cos t$.

5. The equations of the example of §24 with initial conditions
   $x(0) = 0$, $x'(0) = 0$, $y(0) = 1$, $y'(0) = 0$.
   
   Ans. $x(t) = -t - \frac{5}{3}\sin t + \frac{4}{3}\sin 2t$,
   $y(t) = 1 + \frac{2}{3}\cos t - \frac{2}{3}\cos 2t$.

**6.** The equations of the example of §24 with initial conditions
$x(0) = 9$, $x'(0) = 2$, $y(0) = 1$, $y'(0) = 0$.

> *Ans.* $x(t) = -t + 15 \cos t - 5 \sin t - 6 \cos 2t + 4 \sin 2t$,
> $y(t) = 1 + 2 \cos t + 6 \sin t - 2 \cos 2t - 3 \sin 2t$.

**7.** $x''(t) + y'(t) - y(t) = 0$,
$2x'(t) - x(t) + z'(t) - z(t) = 0$,
$x'(t) + 3x(t) + y'(t) - 4y(t) + 3z(t) = 0$;
$x(0) = 0$, $x'(0) = 1$, $y(0) = 0$, $z(0) = 0$.

> *Ans.* $x(t) = e^t - 1$,
> $y(t) = -te^t$,
> $z(t) = 1 - e^t - te^t$.

**8.** $x''(t) - x(t) + 5y'(t) = \beta(t)$,
$y''(t) - 4y(t) - 2x'(t) = 0$,
in which
$$\beta(t) = 6t, \qquad 0 \le t \le 2,$$
$$= 12, \qquad t > 2;$$
$x(0) = 0$, $x'(0) = 0$, $y(0) = 0$, $y'(0) = 0$.

> *Ans.* $x(t) = -2(3t - 5 \sin t + \sin 2t)$
> $+ 2[3(t - 2) - 5 \sin(t - 2) + \sin 2(t - 2)]\alpha(t - 2)$,
> $y(t) = 3 - 4 \cos t + \cos 2t$
> $- [3 - 4 \cos(t - 2) + \cos 2(t - 2)]\alpha(t - 2)$.

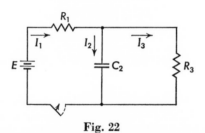

**Fig. 22**

**9.** In Fig. 22 let $E = 60$ volts, $R_1 = 10$ ohms, $R_3 = 20$ ohms, and $C_2 = 5(10)^{-4}$ farad. Determine the currents if when the switch is closed the capacitor carries a charge of 0.03 coulomb.

> *Ans.* $I_1 = 2(1 - e^{-300t})$, $I_2 = -3e^{-300t}$, $I_3 = 2 + e^{-300t}$.

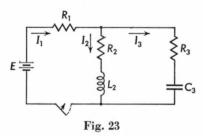

**Fig. 23**

**10.** In Ex. 9 let the initial charge on the capacitor be 0.01 coulomb, but leave the rest of the problem unchanged.

> *Ans.* $I_1 = 2(1 + e^{-300t})$, $I_2 = 3e^{-300t}$, $I_3 = 2 - e^{-300t}$.

**11.** For the network in Fig. 23 set up the equations for the determination of the charge $Q_3$ and the currents $I_1$, $I_2$, $I_3$.   Assume all four of those quantities zero at time zero.   Transform the problem into algebraic form.

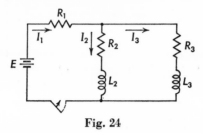

Fig. 24

**12.** For the network in Fig. 24 set up the equations for the determination of the currents.   Assume all currents zero at time zero.   Find $i_1(s) = L\{I_1(t)\}$ and discuss the character of $I_1(t)$ without finding the function explicitly.

# Additional Properties of
# the Transform

## 26. *Power Series Methods*

Certain elementary power series expansions will now be listed for reference:

$$(1) \qquad \frac{1}{1-x} = \sum_{n=0}^{\infty} x^n, \qquad |x| < 1;$$

$$(2) \qquad e^x = \sum_{n=0}^{\infty} \frac{x^n}{n!}, \qquad \text{all } x;$$

$$(3) \qquad \cos x = \sum_{n=0}^{\infty} \frac{(-1)^n x^{2n}}{(2n)!}, \qquad \text{all } x;$$

$$(4) \qquad \sin x = \sum_{n=0}^{\infty} \frac{(-1)^n x^{2n+1}}{(2n+1)!}, \qquad \text{all } x;$$

$$(5) \qquad \cosh x = \sum_{n=0}^{\infty} \frac{x^{2n}}{(2n)!}, \qquad \text{all } x;$$

$$(6) \qquad \sinh x = \sum_{n=0}^{\infty} \frac{x^{2n+1}}{(2n+1)!}, \qquad \text{all } x;$$

$$(7) \qquad \text{Arctan } x = \sum_{n=0}^{\infty} \frac{(-1)^n x^{2n+1}}{2n+1}, \qquad |x| < 1;$$

$$(8) \quad \frac{1}{(1-x)^m} = 1 + \sum_{n=1}^{\infty} \frac{m(m+1) \cdots (m+n-1)x^n}{n!}, \qquad |x| < 1;$$

$$(9) \qquad \ln(1+x) = \sum_{n=0}^{\infty} \frac{(-1)^n x^{n+1}}{n+1}, \qquad |x| < 1;$$

$$(10) \qquad \ln\frac{1 + x}{1 - x} = 2 \sum_{n=0}^{\infty} \frac{x^{2n+1}}{2n + 1}, \qquad |x| < 1.$$

In seeking the Laplace transform, or the inverse transform, of a given function we may find it inconvenient, difficult, or even beyond us to obtain the desired result by direct use of the theorems of Chapters 1 and 2 in a finite number of steps. Then we frequently turn to infinite series. If we can expand our function into a series such that we know how to obtain the desired transform or inverse transform of each term, we can thus solve our original problem.

*Example (a).* Given that $L^{-1}\{f(s)\} = F(t)$, evaluate

$$L^{-1}\left\{\frac{f(s)}{\sinh (cs)}\right\}.$$

We know that $\sinh z = \frac{1}{2}(e^z - e^{-z})$. Then

$$(11) \qquad \frac{f(s)}{\sinh (cs)} = \frac{2f(s)}{e^{cs} - e^{-cs}}.$$

For $h > 0$, $s > 0$, we know how to evaluate $L^{-1}\{e^{-hs}f(s)\}$ by Theorem 15, page 26. Indeed,

$$(12) \qquad L^{-1}\{e^{-hs}f(s)\} = F(t - h)\alpha(t - h), \qquad h > 0, \quad s > 0.$$

We therefore rewrite (11) as

$$(13) \qquad \frac{f(s)}{\sinh (cs)} = \frac{2f(s)e^{-cs}}{1 - e^{-2cs}}$$

because we can use the power series (1) to expand $(1 - e^{-2cs})^{-1}$ in a series of exponentials with negative arguments. From (1) we get

$$\frac{1}{1 - e^{-2cs}} = \sum_{n=0}^{\infty} \exp(-2ncs)$$

so that by (13),

$$(14) \qquad \frac{f(s)}{\sinh (cs)} = 2 \sum_{n=0}^{\infty} f(s) \exp(-2ncs - cs).$$

We now use (12) to obtain, for $c > 0$ $s > 0$,

$$(15) \qquad L^{-1}\frac{f(s)}{\sinh (cs)} = 2 \sum_{n=0}^{\infty} F(t - 2nc - c)\alpha(t - 2nc - c).$$

It is important to realize that the series on the right in (15) is a finite series. No matter how large the value of $t$ nor how small the (positive) $c$, the argument of the $\alpha$ function will become negative for sufficiently large $n$ and for all succeeding $n$-values. Thus each term of the series will be zero for all $n$ such that $(2n + 1)c > t$.

The procedure used in this example is of value to us in applications involving boundary value problems in partial differential equations in Chapter 6.

*Example (b):*   Evaluate $L\left\{\dfrac{1 - e^{-t}}{t}\right\}$.

By (2) we obtain

$$e^{-t} = \sum_{n=0}^{\infty} \frac{(-1)^n t^n}{n!} = 1 + \sum_{n=1}^{\infty} \frac{(-1)^n t^n}{n!}.$$

Therefore we may write

$$\frac{1 - e^{-t}}{t} = \sum_{n=1}^{\infty} \frac{(-1)^{n+1} t^{n-1}}{n!}.$$

A shift in index from $n$ to $(n + 1)$ yields

$$\frac{1 - e^{-t}}{t} = \sum_{n=0}^{\infty} \frac{(-1)^n t^n}{(n+1)!}.$$

We know that $L\left\{\dfrac{t^n}{n!}\right\} = \dfrac{1}{s^{n+1}}.$   Hence

$$L\left\{\frac{1 - e^{-t}}{t}\right\} = \sum_{n=0}^{\infty} \frac{(-1)^n}{(n + 1)s^{n+1}},$$

so that comparison with (9) above yields

(16) $$\qquad L\left\{\frac{1 - e^{-t}}{t}\right\} = \ln\left(1 + \frac{1}{s}\right), \qquad s > 0.$$

The restriction $s > 0$ may be obtained by examining the integral definition of the left member of (16).   Note also the connection with Ex. 15, page 20.

*Example (c).*   Evaluate $L^{-1}\left\{\ln \dfrac{s + 1}{s - 1}\right\}$.

From (10) we have

$$\ln \frac{s + 1}{s - 1} = \ln \frac{1 + \dfrac{1}{s}}{1 - \dfrac{1}{s}} = 2 \sum_{n=0}^{\infty} \frac{1}{(2n + 1)s^{2n+1}}.$$

Now $L^{-1}\left\{\dfrac{1}{s^{2n+1}}\right\} = \dfrac{t^{2n}}{(2n)!}.$   Hence

$$L^{-1}\left\{\ln \frac{s + 1}{s - 1}\right\} = 2 \sum_{n=0}^{\infty} \frac{t^{2n}}{(2n + 1)!},$$

which, with the aid of (6), yields

(17) $$\qquad L^{-1}\left\{\ln \frac{s + 1}{s - 1}\right\} = \frac{2}{t} \sinh t.$$

## EXERCISES

**1.** Evaluate $L\left\{\dfrac{\sin kt}{t}\right\}$, $\qquad\qquad$ *Ans.* Arctan $\dfrac{k}{s}$, $\quad s > 0$.

**2.** Evaluate $L\left\{\dfrac{1 - \cos kt}{t}\right\}$. $\qquad$ *Ans.* $\frac{1}{2}\ln\left(1 + \dfrac{k^2}{s^2}\right)$. $\quad s > k > 0$.

**3.** Evaluate $L\left\{\dfrac{\sinh (kt)}{t}\right\}$. $\qquad$ *Ans.* $\frac{1}{2}\ln\dfrac{s + k}{s - k}$, $\quad s > k > 0$.

**4.** Evaluate $L\left\{\dfrac{1 - \cosh(kt)}{t}\right\}$. $\qquad$ *Ans.* $\frac{1}{2}\ln\left(1 - \dfrac{k^2}{s^2}\right)$, $\quad s > k > 0$.

**5.** Evaluate $F(t) = L^{-1}\left\{\dfrac{1}{s^3(1 - e^{-2s})}\right\}$ and compute $F(5)$.

$$\textit{Ans. } F(t) = \tfrac{1}{2}\sum_{n=0}^{\infty}(t - 2n)^2\alpha(t - 2n); \; F(5) = 17.5.$$

**6.** Evaluate $F(t) = L^{-1}\left\{\dfrac{1}{s^3\cosh(2s)}\right\}$ and compute $F(12)$.

$$\textit{Ans. } F(t) = \sum_{n=0}^{\infty}(-1)^n(t - 4n - 2)^2\alpha(t - 4n - 2); \; F(12) = 68.$$

**7.** Let $\varphi(t) = L^{-1}\left\{\dfrac{3}{s^4\sinh(3s)}\right\}$. Compute $\varphi(10)$. $\qquad$ *Ans.* 344.

**8.** Let $c > 0$, $s > 0$, and let $L^{-1}\{f(s)\} = F(t)$. Prove that

$$L^{-1}\left\{\dfrac{f(s)}{\cosh(cs)}\right\} = 2\sum_{n=0}^{\infty}(-1)^nF(t - 2nc - c)\alpha(t - 2nc - c).$$

**9.** Let $c > 0$, $s > 0$, and let $L^{-1}\{f(s)\} = F(t)$. Prove that

$$L^{-1}\{f(s)\tanh(cs)\} = F(t) + 2\sum_{n=1}^{\infty}(-1)^nF(t - 2nc)\alpha(t - 2nc).$$

**10.** Let $0 < x < 1$, where $x$ does not depend on $s$.
Find the inverse transform $y(x, t)$ of

$$\dfrac{4e^{xs}}{s^3(e^s + e^{-s})}$$

and then compute $y(\frac{1}{2}, 5)$, assuming continuity of $y$. $\qquad$ *Ans.* $y(\frac{1}{2}, 5) = 28.5$.

**11.** In Ex. 4, page 60, replace the alternating current element $E \sin \omega t$ by $EQ(t, c)$ in which $Q$ is the square wave function of Fig. 4, page 18.

$$\textit{Ans. } I(t) = \dfrac{E}{R}\exp\left(-\dfrac{t}{RC}\right) + \dfrac{2E}{R}\sum_{n=1}^{\infty}(-1)^n\exp\left(-\dfrac{t - nc}{RC}\right)\alpha(t - nc).$$

**12.** In Ex. 4, page 60, replace $E \sin \omega t$ by $E\,F(t)$ in which $F(t)$ is the half-wave rectification of $\sin \omega t$ as described in Ex. 13, page 19.

$$\textit{Ans. } I(t) = \dfrac{E}{\omega CZ^2}\sum_{n=0}^{\infty}\left[(-1)^n(\cos \omega t + \omega RC \sin \omega t) - \exp\left(-\dfrac{\omega t - n\pi}{\omega RC}\right)\right]\alpha\left(t - \dfrac{n\pi}{\omega}\right).$$

## 27. *The Error Function*

The error function, abbreviated "erf," is defined by

$$(1) \qquad \operatorname{erf} x = \frac{2}{\sqrt{\pi}} \int_0^x \exp(-\beta^2)\, d\beta.$$

This function arises in many ways. It is sometimes* studied in elementary courses. We also encounter erf $x$ in evaluating inverse transforms of certain simple functions of $s$.

We know that $L^{-1}\{s^{-\frac{1}{2}}\} = (\pi t)^{-\frac{1}{2}}$ and therefore that

$$L^{-1}\left\{\frac{1}{\sqrt{s+1}}\right\} = \frac{e^{-t}}{\sqrt{\pi t}}.$$

Then the convolution theorem yields

$$(2) \qquad L^{-1}\left\{\frac{1}{s\sqrt{s+1}}\right\} = \int_0^t 1 \cdot \frac{e^{-\beta}}{\sqrt{\pi \beta}}\, d\beta.$$

On the right in (2) put $\sqrt{\beta} = \gamma$. Then $\beta^{-\frac{1}{2}}\, d\beta = 2d\gamma$ and we obtain

$$L^{-1}\left\{\frac{1}{s\sqrt{s+1}}\right\} = \frac{2}{\sqrt{\pi}} \int_0^{\sqrt{t}} \exp(-\gamma^2)\, d\gamma.$$

That is,

$$(3) \qquad L^{-1}\left\{\frac{1}{s\sqrt{s+1}}\right\} = \operatorname{erf}(\sqrt{t}).$$

A few basic properties of erf $x$ are useful in our work and will now be obtained. Directly from the definition (1) it follows that the derivative of erf $x$ is given by

$$(4) \qquad \frac{d}{dx} \operatorname{erf} x = \frac{2}{\sqrt{\pi}} \exp(-x^2).$$

From (1) and the power series for $\exp(-\beta^2)$ we get

$$(5) \qquad \operatorname{erf} x = \frac{2}{\sqrt{\pi}} \sum_{n=0}^{\infty} \frac{(-1)^n x^{2n+1}}{(2n+1)n!}.$$

In elementary calculus we found that

$$(6) \qquad \int_0^{\infty} \exp(-\beta^2)\, d\beta = \frac{\sqrt{\pi}}{2}.$$

---

*See E. D. Rainville, *Unified Calculus and Analytic Geometry*, New York, Macmillan, 1961, pp. 605–607, or C. E. Love and E. D. Rainville, *Differential and Integral Calculus*, 6th ed., New York, Macmillan, 1962, pp. 467–470.

From (6) we get

(7)
$$\text{Lim}_{x \to \infty} \text{erf } x = 1.$$

The values of erf $x$ are easily computed for small $x$ from (5) above and for larger $x$ from the asymptotic expansion*

(8)
$$\text{erf } x \sim 1 - \frac{\exp(-x^2)}{\sqrt{\pi}} \sum_{n=0}^{\infty} \frac{(-1)^n[1 \cdot 3 \cdot 5 \cdots (2n-1)]}{2^n x^{2n+1}}.$$

It is convenient in our work to use what is called the complementary error function, denoted by erfc $x$ and defined by

(9)
$$\text{erfc } x = 1 - \text{erf } x,$$

which means also that

(10)
$$\text{erfc } x = \frac{2}{\sqrt{\pi}} \int_x^{\infty} \exp(-\beta^2) \, d\beta.$$

The properties of erf $x$ are readily converted to properties of erfc $x$. It is important that for any fixed $m$,

(11)
$$\text{Lim}_{x \to \infty} x^m \text{ erfc } x = 0,$$

which the student can demonstrate by considering the indeterminate form

$$\frac{\text{erfc } x}{x^{-m}}$$

and using the derivative of erfc $x$ as obtained from (4) above. See the exercises at the end of this section for other properties of erf $x$ and erfc $x$.

A transform which is important in certain applications (§§33, 34) is

$$L\left\{\text{erfc}\left(\frac{k}{\sqrt{t}}\right)\right\}$$

in which $k$ is to be independent of $t$ and $k > 0$.

By the definition of erfc $x$ we have

(12)
$$\text{erfc}\left(\frac{k}{\sqrt{t}}\right) = \frac{2}{\sqrt{\pi}} \int_{\frac{k}{\sqrt{t}}}^{\infty} \exp(-\beta^2) \, d\beta.$$

In (12) put $\beta = \dfrac{k}{\sqrt{v}}$ so that the limits of integration become $v = t$ to $v = 0$

*See, for example, E. D. Rainville, *Special Functions*, New York, Macmillan, 1960, pp. 36–38. The function erf $x$ is tabulated under the name "The Probability Integral," in B. O. Peirce and R. M. Foster, *A Short Table of Integrals*, 4th ed., New York, Ginn, 1956, pp. 128–132.

Since $d\beta = -\frac{1}{2}kv^{-\frac{3}{2}}\,dv$, we obtain (using the minus sign to reverse the order of integration)

$$(13) \qquad \operatorname{erfc}\left(\frac{k}{\sqrt{t}}\right) = \frac{k}{\sqrt{\pi}}\int_0^t v^{-\frac{3}{2}}\exp\left(-\frac{k^2}{v}\right)dv.$$

The integral on the right in (13) is a convolution integral. Hence

$$L\left\{\operatorname{erfc}\left(\frac{k}{\sqrt{t}}\right)\right\} = \frac{k}{\sqrt{\pi}}L\{1\}\cdot L\left\{t^{-\frac{3}{2}}\exp\left(-\frac{k^2}{t}\right)\right\},$$

or

$$(14) \qquad L\left\{\operatorname{erfc}\left(\frac{k}{\sqrt{t}}\right)\right\} = \frac{k}{s\sqrt{\pi}}L\left\{t^{-\frac{3}{2}}\exp\left(-\frac{k^2}{t}\right)\right\}.$$

Now let

$$(15) \qquad A(s) = L\left\{t^{-\frac{3}{2}}\exp\left(-\frac{k^2}{t}\right)\right\}.$$

Note that the functions $t^m \exp\left(-\dfrac{k^2}{t}\right)$ are of class A, page 10, for each $m$.

From (15) it follows, by Theorem 9, that

$$(16) \qquad \frac{dA}{ds} = L\left\{-t^{-\frac{1}{2}}\exp\left(-\frac{k^2}{t}\right)\right\}$$

and

$$(17) \qquad \frac{d^2A}{ds^2} = L\left\{t^{\frac{1}{2}}\exp\left(-\frac{k^2}{t}\right)\right\}.$$

But also, by Theorem 5,

$$L\left\{\frac{d}{dt}\,t^{\frac{1}{2}}\exp\left(-\frac{k^2}{t}\right)\right\} = sL\left\{t^{\frac{1}{2}}\exp\left(-\frac{k^2}{t}\right)\right\} - \lim_{t\to 0^+}\left[t^{\frac{1}{2}}\exp\left(-\frac{k^2}{t}\right)\right],$$

or

$$(18) \quad L\left\{\frac{1}{2}t^{-\frac{1}{2}}\exp\left(-\frac{k^2}{t}\right) + k^2 t^{-\frac{3}{2}}\exp\left(-\frac{k^2}{t}\right)\right\} = sL\left\{t^{\frac{1}{2}}\exp\left(-\frac{k^2}{t}\right)\right\} - 0.$$

Because of (15), (16), and (17) equation (18) may be written

$$-\frac{1}{2}\frac{dA}{ds} + k^2A = s\frac{d^2A}{ds^2}.$$

Therefore the desired function $A(s)$ is a solution of the differential equation

$$(19) \qquad s\frac{d^2A}{ds^2} + \frac{1}{2}\frac{dA}{ds} - k^2A = 0.$$

We need two boundary conditions to go with equation (19). We know that as $s \to \infty$, $A \to 0$. Now consider what happens as $s \to 0^+$.

By (15),

$$\underset{s \to 0+}{\text{Lim}} A(s) = \underset{s \to 0+}{\text{Lim}} \int_0^\infty e^{-st} t^{-\frac{3}{2}} \exp\left(-\frac{k^2}{t}\right) dt$$

$$= \int_0^\infty t^{-\frac{3}{2}} \exp\left(-\frac{k^2}{t}\right) dt.$$

Equation (13) yields (with $y$ replacing $t$)

(20)          $$\int_0^y v^{-\frac{3}{2}} \exp\left(-\frac{k^2}{v}\right) dv = \frac{\sqrt{\pi}}{k} \operatorname{erfc}\left(\frac{k}{\sqrt{y}}\right).$$

Therefore

$$\underset{s \to 0+}{\text{Lim}} A(s) = \frac{\sqrt{\pi}}{k} \underset{y \to \infty}{\text{Lim}} \operatorname{erfc}\left(\frac{k}{\sqrt{y}}\right) = \frac{\sqrt{\pi}}{k} \operatorname{erfc} 0 = \frac{\sqrt{\pi}}{k}.$$

To get the general solution of the differential equation (19) we change independent variable* from $s$ to $z = \sqrt{s}$. Now by the chain rule of elementary calculus,

$$\frac{dA}{ds} = \frac{dz}{ds}\frac{dA}{dz} = \frac{1}{2\sqrt{s}}\frac{dA}{dz} = \frac{1}{2z}\frac{dA}{dz},$$

$$\frac{d^2A}{ds^2} = \frac{1}{4s}\frac{d^2A}{dz^2} - \frac{1}{4s\sqrt{s}}\frac{dA}{dz}.$$

Thus

$$s\frac{d^2A}{ds^2} = \frac{1}{4}\frac{d^2A}{dz^2} - \frac{1}{4z}\frac{dA}{dz}$$

and equation (19) becomes

(21)          $$\frac{d^2A}{dz^2} - 4k^2A = 0.$$

The general solution of (21) is

$$A = b_1 \exp(-2kz) + b_2 \exp(2kz),$$

so that the general solution of (19) is

(22)          $$A = b_1 \exp(-2k\sqrt{s}) + b_2 \exp(2k\sqrt{s}).$$

We must determine the constants $b_1$ and $b_2$ from the conditions that $A \to 0$ as $s \to \infty$ and $A \to \sqrt{\pi}/k$ as $s \to 0+$. As $s \to \infty$, $A$ will not approach a

---

*Such a change of variable is dictated by the test on page 13 of E. D. Rainville, *Intermediate Differential Equations*, New York, Wiley, 1943.

limit unless $b_2 = 0$.   Then, letting $s \to 0^+$, we get

$$\frac{\sqrt{\pi}}{k} = b_1.$$

Therefore

$$A(s) = L\left\{t^{-\frac{3}{2}} \exp\left(-\frac{k^2}{t}\right)\right\} = \frac{\sqrt{\pi}}{k} \exp(-2k\sqrt{s}).$$

We return to (14) to write the desired transform

(23) $$L\left\{\mathrm{erfc}\left(\frac{k}{\sqrt{t}}\right)\right\} = \frac{1}{s} \exp(-2k\sqrt{s}), \quad k > 0, \quad s > 0.$$

We shall use (23) in the form

(24) $$L^{-1}\left\{\frac{1}{s} \exp(-2k\sqrt{s})\right\} = \mathrm{erfc}\left(\frac{k}{\sqrt{t}}\right), \quad k > 0, \quad s > 0.$$

In Chapter 6 it will be important to combine the use of equation (24) and the series methods of §26.

Consider the problem of obtaining

(25) $$L^{-1}\left\{\frac{\sinh(x\sqrt{s})}{s \sinh \sqrt{s}}\right\}. \quad 0 < x < 1, \quad s > 0.$$

If $x$ were greater than unity, the inverse in (25) would not exist because of the behavior of $\sinh(x\sqrt{s})/\sinh\sqrt{s}$ as $s \to \infty$.

Because we know (24) it is wise to turn to exponentials.  We write

(26) $$\frac{\sinh(x\sqrt{s})}{\sinh\sqrt{s}} = \frac{\exp(x\sqrt{s}) - \exp(-x\sqrt{s})}{\exp(\sqrt{s}) - \exp(-\sqrt{s})}.$$

As in §26 we seek a series involving exponentials of negative argument. We therefore multiply numerator and denominator on the right in (26) by $\exp(-\sqrt{s})$ and find that

(27) $$\frac{\sinh(x\sqrt{s})}{\sinh\sqrt{s}} = \frac{\exp[-(1-x)\sqrt{s}] - \exp[-(1+x)\sqrt{s}]}{1 - \exp(-2\sqrt{s})}.$$

Now

(28) $$\frac{1}{1 - \exp(-2\sqrt{s})} = \sum_{n=0}^{\infty} \exp(-2n\sqrt{s}).$$

Therefore,

$$\frac{\sinh(x\sqrt{s})}{s\sinh\sqrt{s}} = \sum_{n=0}^{\infty} \frac{1}{s}\{\exp[-(1-x+2n)\sqrt{s}] - \exp[-(1+x+2n)\sqrt{s}]\}.$$

For $0 < x < 1$ the exponentials have negative arguments and we may use (24) to conclude that

$$(29) \quad L^{-1}\left\{\frac{\sinh(x\sqrt{s})}{s \sinh \sqrt{s}}\right\} = \sum_{n=0}^{\infty}\left[\operatorname{erfc}\left(\frac{1 - x + 2n}{2\sqrt{t}}\right) - \operatorname{erfc}\left(\frac{1 + x + 2n}{2\sqrt{t}}\right)\right].$$

## EXERCISES

**1.** Show that for all real $x$, $|\operatorname{erf} x| < 1$.

**2.** Show that erf $x$ is an odd function of $x$.

**3.** Show that $\operatorname*{Lim}_{x \to 0} \dfrac{\operatorname{erf} x}{x} = \dfrac{2}{\sqrt{\pi}}$.

**4.** Use integration by parts to show that

$$\int_0^x \operatorname{erf} y \, dy = x \operatorname{erf} x - \frac{1}{\sqrt{\pi}}\left[1 - \exp(-x^2)\right].$$

**5.** Obtain equation (11), page 77.

**6.** Start with the power series for erf $x$, equation (5), page 76, and show that

$$L\{t^{-\frac{1}{2}} \operatorname{erf}(\sqrt{t})\} = \frac{2}{\sqrt{\pi s}} \operatorname{Arctan} \frac{1}{\sqrt{s}}, \quad s > 0.$$

**7.** Use the fact that

$$\frac{1}{1 + \sqrt{1 + s}} = \frac{1 - \sqrt{1 + s}}{1 - (1 + s)} = -\frac{1}{s} + \frac{\sqrt{1 + s}}{s} = -\frac{1}{s} + \frac{1 + s}{s\sqrt{1 + s}}$$

and equation (3), page 76, to show that

$$L^{-1}\left\{\frac{1}{1 + \sqrt{1 + s}}\right\} = -1 + \operatorname{erf}(\sqrt{t}) + \frac{e^{-t}}{\sqrt{\pi t}}$$

$$= \frac{e^{-t}}{\sqrt{\pi t}} - \operatorname{erfc}(\sqrt{t}).$$

**8.** Use equation (3), page 76, to conclude that

$$L^{-1}\left\{\frac{1}{(s - 1)\sqrt{s}}\right\} = e^t \operatorname{erf}(\sqrt{t})$$

and therefore that

$$L^{-1}\left\{\frac{1}{\sqrt{s}(\sqrt{s} + 1)}\right\} = e^t \operatorname{erfc}(\sqrt{t}).$$

**9.** Evaluate $L^{-1}\left\{\dfrac{1}{\sqrt{s} + 1}\right\}$.        *Ans.* $\dfrac{1}{\sqrt{\pi t}} - e^t \operatorname{erfc}(\sqrt{t})$.

**10.** Evaluate $L^{-1}\left\{\dfrac{1}{\sqrt{s} - 1}\right\}$.        *Ans.* $\dfrac{1}{\sqrt{\pi t}} + e^t + e^t \operatorname{erf}(\sqrt{t})$.

**11.** Define the function $\varphi(t)$ by

$$\varphi(t) = L^{-1}\left\{\operatorname{erf}\frac{1}{s}\right\}.$$

Prove that

$$L\left\{\varphi(\sqrt{t})\right\} = \frac{2}{\sqrt{\pi s}}\sin\frac{1}{\sqrt{s}}.$$

**12.** Show that, for $x > 0$,

$$L^{-1}\left\{\frac{\operatorname{sech} x\sqrt{s}}{s}\right\} = 2\sum_{n=0}^{\infty}(-1)^n\operatorname{erfc}\left[\frac{(2n+1)x}{2\sqrt{t}}\right].$$

**13.** Show that, for $x > 0$,

$$L^{-1}\left\{\frac{\operatorname{csch} x\sqrt{s}}{s}\right\} = 2\sum_{n=0}^{\infty}\operatorname{erfc}\left[\frac{(2n+1)x}{2\sqrt{t}}\right].$$

## 28. Bessel Functions

The Bessel function

$$(1) \qquad J_n(z) = \sum_{k=0}^{\infty}\frac{(-1)^k(\frac{1}{2}z)^{2k+n}}{k!\,\Gamma(k+n+1)},$$

of the first kind and of index $n$, appears frequently in both pure and applied mathematics. We meet $J_n(z)$ in a simple application of the series technique of §26. If we can expand a given function of $s$ in negative powers of $s$, surely we can get the inverse transform term by term. A simple example is the following:

$$\frac{1}{s}\exp\left(-\frac{x}{s}\right) = \sum_{k=0}^{\infty}\frac{(-1)^k x^k}{k!\,s^{k+1}}$$

which leads immediately to

$$(2) \qquad L^{-1}\left\{\frac{1}{s}\exp\left(-\frac{x}{s}\right)\right\} = \sum_{k=0}^{\infty}\frac{(-1)^k x^k t^k}{k!\,k!}.$$

When $n = 0$ in (1) we get, since $\Gamma(k+1) = k!$,

$$(3) \qquad J_0(z) = \sum_{k=0}^{\infty}\frac{(-1)^k(\frac{1}{2}z)^{2k}}{k!\,k!}.$$

By comparing (2) with (3) we get

$$(4) \qquad L^{-1}\left\{\frac{1}{s}\exp\left(-\frac{x}{s}\right)\right\} = J_0(2\sqrt{xt}); \qquad x > 0, \quad s > 0.$$

From

$$\frac{1}{s^{n+1}}\exp\left(-\frac{x}{s}\right) = \sum_{k=0}^{\infty}\frac{(-1)^k x^k}{k!\,s^{k+n+1}}$$

we get

$$L^{-1}\left\{\frac{1}{s^{n+1}}\exp\left(-\frac{x}{s}\right)\right\} = \sum_{k=0}^{\infty}\frac{(-1)^k x^k t^{k+n}}{k!\,\Gamma(k+n+1)}$$

$$= x^{-\frac{1}{2}n}t^{\frac{1}{2}n}\sum_{k=0}^{\infty}\frac{(-1)^k(\sqrt{xt})^{2k+n}}{k!\,\Gamma(k+n+1)}.$$

Therefore, at least for $n \geqq 0$,

$$(5) \qquad L^{-1}\left\{\frac{1}{s^{n+1}}\exp\left(-\frac{x}{s}\right)\right\} = \left(\frac{t}{x}\right)^{\frac{1}{2}n}J_n(2\sqrt{xt}), \qquad s > 0, \quad x > 0.$$

With more knowledge of the Gamma function we could use series methods to obtain the transform of $J_n(xt)$ for general $n$. Here we restrict ourselves to $n = 0$ for simplicity.

From (1) we obtain

$$J_0(xt) = \sum_{k=0}^{\infty}\frac{(-1)^k(\frac{1}{2}x)^{2k}t^{2k}}{k!\,k!}.$$

Then

$$L\{J_0(xt)\} = \sum_{k=0}^{\infty}\frac{(-1)^k(\frac{1}{2}x)^{2k}(2k)!}{k!\,k!\,s^{2k+1}}.$$

But $(2k)! = 2^k k![1\cdot 3\cdot 5\cdots(2k-1)]$. Hence

$$L\{J_0(xt)\} = \frac{1}{s}\left[1 + \sum_{k=1}^{\infty}\frac{(-1)^k[1\cdot 3\cdot 5\cdots(2k-1)]x^{2k}}{2^k\cdot k!\,s^{2k}}\right],$$

or

$$L\{J_0(xt)\} = \frac{1}{s}\left(1 + \frac{x^2}{s^2}\right)^{-\frac{1}{2}}.$$

Therefore

$$(6) \qquad L\{J_0(xt)\} = \frac{1}{\sqrt{s^2+x^2}}.$$

From (1) it is easy to conclude that

$$\frac{d}{dz}J_0(z) = -J_1(z).$$

Then

$$\frac{d}{dt}J_0(xt) = -xJ_1(xt)$$

and we obtain

$$L\{-xJ_1(xt)\} = L\left\{\frac{d}{dt}J_0(xt)\right\}$$

$$= s\,L\{J_0(xt)\} - J_0(0).$$

But $J_0(0) = 1$, so

$$L\{-xJ_1(xt)\} = \frac{s}{\sqrt{s^2 + x^2}} - 1,$$

or

(7)       $$L\{J_1(xt)\} = \frac{\sqrt{s^2 + x^2} - s}{x\sqrt{s^2 + x^2}}.$$

**EXERCISE**

1. The modified Bessel function of the first kind and of index $n$ is

$$I_n(z) = \sum_{k=0}^{\infty} \frac{(\tfrac{1}{2}z)^{2k+n}}{k!\,\Gamma(k + n + 1)}.$$

Show that

$$L^{-1}\left\{\frac{1}{s^{n+1}} \exp\!\left(\frac{x}{s}\right)\right\} = \left(\frac{t}{x}\right)^{\frac{1}{2}n} I_n(2\sqrt{xt})$$

## 29. *Differential Equations with Variable Coefficients*

Any reader who has become overly optimistic about the efficacy of the Laplace transform as a tool in treating linear differential equations should keep in mind that we have restricted our work so far to equations with constant coefficients.

Suppose that we are confronted with a boundary value problem involving the equation

(1)       $$F''(t) + t^2 F(t) = 0,$$

Let $L\{F(t)\} = f(s)$ and put $F(0) = A$, $F'(0) = B$.   Then application of the operator $L$ transforms equation (1) into

$$s^2 f(s) - sA - B + \frac{d^2}{ds^2} f(s) = 0,$$

or

(2)       $$f''(s) + s^2 f(s) = As + B.$$

The problem of getting the complementary function for equation (2) is the same as it is for equation (1); no progress has been made.   The left member of (1) remained essentially unchanged under the Laplace transformation.

The behavior of (1) under $L$ is not unique.   Indeed, the differential equations with polynomial coefficients which remain invariant under the Laplace transformation have been* classified

---

*E. D. Rainville, "Linear differential invariance under an operator related to the Laplace transformation," *Amer. Journal of Math.*, 1940, vol. 62, pp. 391–405.

Since $L\{t^n F(t)\} = (-1)^n \dfrac{d^n}{ds^n} f(s)$, it follows that the operator $L$ can be used to transform a differential equation with polynomial coefficients into a differential equation with polynomial coefficients and that the order of the new equation will equal the maximum degree of the polynomial coefficients in the original equation. The Laplace transform is simply not the proper tool for attacking differential equations with variable coefficients. For such a purpose the classical method of solution by power series is a good tool to use.

# Partial Differential Equations

## 30. Boundary Value Problems

For some boundary value problems involving partial differential equations the Laplace transform provides an effective method of attack. For other problems the transform method contributes additional information even when the older techniques, such as separation of variables and Fourier series, may be easier to use. There remain problems for which the Laplace transform method contributes nothing but complications.

In this chapter we present a few applications and a detailed study of the solution of some simple problems. There is here too little space for an attempt at presenting a large number of specific applications. Our goal is to give the student sufficient background to enable him to use the Laplace transform on problems he encounters in practice and to give him some criteria to use in deciding whether the transform method is an appropriate tool for a given problem.

We first solve some artificial problems which have been constructed to exhibit the technique and underlying ideas without introducing the complexities common to many physical applications. The student who fully understands and can execute the solutions of such simple problems will find no difficulty, other than an increase in amount of labor, in solving corresponding problems which arise in physical situations.

*Example.* Solve the problem consisting of the equation

(1) $$\frac{\partial^2 y}{\partial x^2} = 16 \frac{\partial^2 y}{\partial t^2}, \qquad \text{for } t > 0, \quad x > 0;$$

together with the conditions

(2) $\qquad\qquad t \to 0^+, \qquad y \to 0, \quad \text{for } x > 0;$

(3) $\qquad\qquad t \to 0^+, \qquad \dfrac{\partial y}{\partial t} \to -1, \quad \text{for } x > 0;$

(4) $\qquad\qquad x \to 0^+, \qquad y \to t^2, \quad \text{for } t > 0;$

(5) $\qquad\qquad \underset{x \to \infty}{\text{Lim}}\, y(x, t) \text{ exists, for fixed } t > 0.$

Those characteristics of the problem which suggest that it is worthwhile to try the Laplace transform technique are as follows:

(a) The differential equation is linear (necessary),
(b) The equation has constant coefficients (highly desirable),
(c) At least one independent variable has the range 0 to $\infty$ (highly desirable),
(d) There are appropriate initial ($t = 0$) conditions involving the independent variable in (c) above (desirable).

In this problem the independent variable $x$ also has the range 0 to $\infty$ but there is only one condition at $x = 0$: two conditions are needed in transforming a second derivative. We shall therefore attack this problem with Laplace transforms with respect to the variable $t$.
Let

(6) $\qquad\qquad L\{y(x, t)\} = w(x, s),$

in which $x$ is treated as a constant (parameter) insofar as the Laplace transformation is concerned. Since we shall verify our solution there is no risk in assuming that the operations of differentiations with respect to $x$ and Laplace transforms with respect to $t$ are commutative.

Because (1) has constant coefficients, derivatives with respect to the transform variable $s$ will not appear. The partial differential equation (1) will be transformed into an ordinary differential equation with independent variable $x$ and with $s$ involved as a parameter. In view of (6), application of the operator $L$ transforms (1), (2) and (3) into

(7) $\qquad\qquad \dfrac{d^2 w}{dx^2} = 16(s^2 w + 1), \qquad x > 0.$

The conditions (4) and (5) become

(8) $\qquad\qquad x \to 0^+, \qquad w \to \dfrac{2}{s^3},$

(9) $\qquad\qquad \underset{x \to \infty}{\text{Lim}}\, w(x, s) \text{ exists.}$

We now solve the new problem, (7), (8) and (9), for $w(x, s)$ and then obtain $y(x, t)$ as the inverse transform of $w$. Let us rewrite (7) in the form

(10) $\qquad\qquad \dfrac{d^2 w}{dx^2} - 16 s^2 w = 16$

and keep in mind that $x$ is the independent variable and $s$ is a parameter. When we get the general solution of (10) the arbitrary constants in it may well be functions of $s$; they must not involve $x$.

The general solution of (10) should be found by inspection.   It is

$$(11) \quad w = -\frac{1}{s^2} + c_1(s) \exp(-4sx) + c_2(s) \exp(4sx), \quad x > 0, \quad s > 0.$$

Because of (9), the $w$ of (11) is to approach a limit as $x \to \infty$.   The first two terms on the right in (11) approach limits as $x \to \infty$, but the term with the positive exponent, $\exp(4sx)$, will not do so unless

$$(12) \qquad\qquad\qquad\qquad c_2(s) \equiv 0.$$

That is, (9) forces (12) upon us.   The $w$ of (11) then becomes

$$(13) \qquad\qquad w = -\frac{1}{s^2} + c_1(s) \exp(-4sx), \quad x > 0, \quad s > 0.$$

Application of the condition (8) to the $w$ of (13) yields

$$\frac{2}{s^3} = c_1(s) - \frac{1}{s^2}; \quad c_1(s) = \frac{2}{s^3} + \frac{1}{s^2}.$$

Thus we find that

$$(14) \qquad w(x, s) = -\frac{1}{s^2} + \left(\frac{2}{s^3} + \frac{1}{s^2}\right) \exp(-4sx), \quad x > 0, \quad s > 0.$$

We already know that if $L^{-1}\{f(s)\} = F(t)$,

$$(15) \qquad\qquad\qquad L^{-1}\{e^{-cs} f(s)\} = F(t - c)\alpha(t - c).$$

Therefore the application of the operator $L^{-1}$ throughout (14) gives us

$$(16) \quad y(x, t) = -t + [(t - 4x)^2 + (t - 4x)]\alpha(t - 4x), \quad x > 0, \quad t > 0.$$

It is our contention that the $y$ of (16) satisfies the boundary value problem (1)–(5).   Let us now verify the solution in detail.

From (16) it follows that

$$(17) \quad \frac{\partial y}{\partial t} = -1 + [2(t - 4x) + 1]\alpha(t - 4x), \quad x > 0, \quad t > 0, \quad t \neq 4x.$$

Note the discontinuity in the derivative for $t = 4x$.   This is forcing us into the admission that we obtain a solution of the problem only on each side of the line $t = 4x$ in the first quadrant of the $xt$-plane.   Our $y$ will not satisfy the differential equation along that line because the second derivative cannot exist there.   This is a reflection of the fact that (1) is a "hyperbolic differential equation."   Whether the "solution" does or does not satisfy the differential equation along what are called the characteristic lines of the equation depends upon the specific boundary conditions.   We shall treat each problem individually with no attempt to examine the general situation.

From (17) we obtain

(18) $$\frac{\partial^2 y}{\partial t^2} = 2\alpha(t - 4x), \qquad x > 0, \quad t > 0, \quad t \neq 4x.$$

Equation (16) also yields

(19) $$\frac{\partial y}{\partial x} = [-8(t - 4x) - 4]\alpha(t - 4x), \qquad x > 0, \quad t > 0, \quad t \neq 4x,$$

(20) $$\frac{\partial^2 y}{\partial x^2} = 32\alpha(t - 4x), \qquad x > 0, \quad t > 0, \quad t \neq 4x.$$

Equations (18) and (20) combine to show that the $y$ of (16) is a solution of the differential equation (1) in the $xt$ region desired except along the line $t = 4x$ where the second derivatives do not exist.

Next we verify that our $y$ satisfies the boundary conditions. To see whether $y$ satisfies the condition (2) we must hold $x$ fixed, but positive, and then let $t$ approach zero through positive values. As

$$t \to 0^+, \; y \to 0 + [(-4x)^2 + (-4x)]\alpha(-4x) = 0, \quad \text{for } x > 0.$$

Thus (2) is satisfied. Note that $\alpha(-4x)$ would not have been zero for negative $x$.

From (17), with $x$ fixed and positive, it follows that as

$$t \to 0^+, \frac{\partial y}{\partial t} \to -1 + [2(-4x) + 1]\alpha(-4x) = -1, \text{ for } x > 0.$$

Thus (3) is satisfied. Once more the fact that $x$ is positive plays an important role in the verification.

Consider the condition (4). In it we must hold $t$ fixed and positive. Then, by (16), as

$$x \to 0^+, \; y \to -t + (t^2 + t)\alpha(t) = -t + t^2 + t = t^2, \quad \text{for } t > 0.$$

Then (4) is satisfied.

Finally, the $y$ of (16) satisfies the condition (5), since

$$\lim_{x \to \infty} y(x, t) = -t + 0 = -t, \text{ for } t > 0,$$

because for sufficiently large $x$ and fixed $t$, $(t - 4x)$ is negative and therefore $\alpha(t - 4x) = 0$. This completes the verification of the solution (16).

## EXERCISES

In each exercise, solve the problem and verify your solution completely.

1. $\dfrac{\partial y}{\partial x} + 4\dfrac{\partial y}{\partial t} = -8t,$     for $t > 0, \; x > 0$;

    $t \to 0^+, \; y \to 0,$     for $x > 0$;
    $x \to 0^+, \; y \to 2t^2,$     for $t > 0$.

             *Ans.* $y(x, t) = -t^2 + 3(t - 4x)^2\alpha(t - 4x).$

**2.** $\dfrac{\partial y}{\partial x} + 2\dfrac{\partial y}{\partial t} = 4t,$     for $t > 0$ $x > 0$;

$t \to 0^+,\ y \to 0,$     for $x > 0$;

$x \to 0^+,\ y \to 2t^3,$     for $t > 0$.

*Ans.* $y(x, t) = t^2 + [2(t - 2x)^3 - (t - 2x)^2]\alpha(t - 2x).$

**3.** Solve Ex. 1 with the condition as $t \to 0^+$ replaced by $t \to 0^+,\ y \to x$.

*Ans.* $y(x, t) = x - \tfrac{1}{4}t - t^2 + [3(t - 4x)^2 + \tfrac{1}{4}(t - 4x)]\alpha(t - 4x).$

**4.** Solve Ex. 2 with the condition as $t \to 0^+$ replaced by $t \to 0^+,\ y \to 2x$.

*Ans.* $y(x, t) = 2x - t + t^2 + [2(t - 2x)^3 - (t - 2x)^2 + (t - 2x)]\alpha(t - 2x).$

**5.** $\dfrac{\partial^2 y}{\partial x^2} = 16\dfrac{\partial^2 y}{\partial t^2},$     for $t > 0,\ x > 0$;

$t \to 0^+,\ y \to 0,$     for $x > 0$;

$t \to 0^+,\ \dfrac{\partial y}{\partial t} \to -2,$     for $x > 0$;

$x \to 0^+,\ y \to t,$     for $t > 0$;

$\underset{x \to \infty}{\text{Lim}}\ y(x, t)$ exists for $t > 0$.

*Ans.* $y = 3(t - 4x)\alpha(t - 4x) - 2t.$

**6.** $\dfrac{\partial^2 y}{\partial t^2} = 4\dfrac{\partial^2 y}{\partial x^2},$     for $t > 0,\ x > 0$;

$t \to 0^+,\ y \to 0,$     for $x > 0$;

$t \to 0^+,\ \dfrac{\partial y}{\partial t} \to 2,$     for $x > 0$;

$x \to 0^+,\ y \to \sin t,$     for $t > 0$;

$\underset{x \to \infty}{\text{Lim}}\ y(x, t)$ exists for $t > 0$.

*Ans.* $y = 2t + [\sin(t - \tfrac{1}{2}x) - 2(t - \tfrac{1}{2}x)]\alpha(t - \tfrac{1}{2}x).$

## 31. *The Wave Equation*

The transverse displacement $y$ of an elastic string must satisfy the one-dimensional wave equation

$$\frac{\partial^2 y}{\partial t^2} = a^2 \frac{\partial^2 y}{\partial x^2},$$

in which the positive constant $a$ has the dimensions of a velocity, cm. per sec., etc.

Suppose a long elastic string is initially taut and at rest so that we may take, at $t = 0$,

$$y = 0 \quad \text{and} \quad \frac{\partial y}{\partial t} = 0, \quad \text{for } x \geqq 0.$$

We assume the string long enough that the assumption that it extends from $x = 0$ to $\infty$ introduces no appreciable error over the time interval in which we are interested.

Suppose also that that end of the string far distant from the $y$-axis is held fixed, $y \to 0$, as $x \to \infty$, but that at the $y$-axis end the string is moved up and down according to some prescribed law, $y \to F(t)$ as $x \to 0^+$, with $F(t)$ known.

Figure 25 shows the position of the string at some $t > 0$.

The problem of determining the transverse displacement $y$ in terms of $x$ and $t$ is that of solving the boundary value problem:

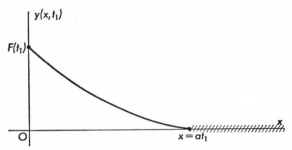

**Fig. 25**

(1)           $$\frac{\partial^2 y}{\partial t^2} = a^2 \frac{\partial^2 y}{\partial x^2}, \qquad \text{for } t > 0, \quad x > 0;$$

(2)           $$t \to 0^+, \qquad y \to 0, \quad \text{for } x \geqq 0;$$

(3)           $$t \to 0^+, \qquad \frac{\partial y}{\partial t} \to 0, \quad \text{for } x > 0;$$

(4)           $$x \to 0^+, \qquad y \to F(t), \quad \text{for } t \geqq 0;$$

(5)           $$\operatorname*{Lim}_{x \to \infty} y(x, t) = 0, \qquad \text{for all } t \geqq 0.$$

The prescribed function $F(t)$ must vanish at $t = 0$ in order to retain continuity of the string.

This problem satisfies the criteria, page 87, which suggest the use of the Laplace transform. Let

(6)           $$L\{y(x, t)\} = u(x, s), \qquad L\{F(t)\} = f(s) .$$

Note that $F(t)$ must be continuous because of its physical meaning here. The operator $L$ converts the problem (1)–(5) into the new problem

(7)           $$s^2 u = a^2 \frac{d^2 u}{dx^2}, \qquad \text{for } x > 0;$$

(8)           $$x \to 0^+, \qquad u \to f(s);$$

(9)           $$\operatorname*{Lim}_{x \to \infty} u(x, s) = 0.$$

From (7) we write at once the general solution

(10)           $$u(x, s) = c_1(s) \exp\left(-\frac{sx}{a}\right) + c_2(s) \exp\left(\frac{sx}{a}\right).$$

With $s > 0$, $x > 0$, the condition (9) requires

(11)                              $c_2(s) \equiv 0.$

Thus (10) becomes

(12)                    $u(x, s) = c_1(s) \exp\left(-\frac{sx}{a}\right)$

and (8) requires that

$$f(s) = c_1(s).$$

We therefore have

(13)          $u(x, s) = f(s) \exp\left(-\frac{sx}{a}\right), \qquad x > 0, \quad s > 0.$

Equation (13) yields the desired solution

(14)          $y(x, t) = F\left(t - \frac{x}{a}\right)\alpha\left(t - \frac{x}{a}\right), \qquad x > 0, \quad t > 0,$

in which we assume that $F(t)$ is defined in some manner for negative argument so that Theorem 15, page 26, can be used.

Verification of the solution (14) is a simple matter. Note that

$$\frac{\partial y}{\partial t} = F'\left(t - \frac{x}{a}\right)\alpha\left(t - \frac{x}{a}\right), \quad \frac{\partial y}{\partial x} = -\frac{1}{a}F'\left(t - \frac{x}{a}\right)\alpha\left(t - \frac{x}{a}\right)$$

and

$$\frac{\partial^2 y}{\partial t^2} = F''\left(t - \frac{x}{a}\right)\alpha\left(t - \frac{x}{a}\right), \quad \frac{\partial^2 y}{\partial x^2} = \frac{1}{a^2}F''\left(t - \frac{x}{a}\right)\alpha\left(t - \frac{x}{a}\right).$$

We are forced to assume existence of two derivatives of the prescribed function $F(t)$. It is particularly convenient to choose $F(t)$ so that $F'(0)$ and $F''(0)$ vanish along with $F(0)$, so that the continuity of $y$ and its derivatives is not interrupted along the line $x = at$. Completion of the verification of the solution is left to the student.

**EXERCISE**

1. Interpret and solve the problem:

$$\frac{\partial^2 y}{\partial t^2} = \frac{\partial^2 y}{\partial x^2}, \qquad \text{for } t > 0, \ 0 < x < 1;$$
$$t \to 0^+, \ y \to x - x^2, \qquad \text{for } 0 < x < 1;$$
$$t \to 0^+, \ \frac{\partial y}{\partial t} \to 0, \qquad \text{for } 0 < x < 1;$$
$$x \to 0^+, \ y \to 0, \qquad \text{for } t > 0;$$
$$x \to 1^-, \ y \to 0, \qquad \text{for } t > 0.$$

Verify your solution directly.

*Ans.* $y = x - x^2 - t^2$

$$+ \sum_{n=0}^{\infty} (-1)^n \lfloor (t - n - x)^2 \alpha(t - n - x) + (t - n - 1 + x)^2 \alpha(t - n - 1 + x) \rfloor.$$

## 32. *The Heat Equation*

Suppose that, for some solid under consideration, $u$ represents the temperature at a point with rectangular coordinates $x$, $y$, $z$ and at time $t$. The origin of coordinates and the initial time $t = 0$ may be assigned at our convenience. If there are no heat sources present, then the temperature $u$ must satisfy the *heat equation*

$$(1) \qquad \frac{\partial u}{\partial t} = h^2 \left( \frac{\partial^2 u}{\partial x^2} + \frac{\partial^2 u}{\partial y^2} + \frac{\partial^2 u}{\partial z^2} \right),$$

in which

$$x, y, z = \text{rectangular space coordinates,}$$
$$t = \text{time coordinate,}$$
$$h^2 = \text{thermal diffusivity,}$$
$$u = \text{temperature.}$$

The constant $h^2$ and the variables $x$, $y$, $z$, $t$, $u$ may be in any consistent set of units. For instance, we may measure $x$, $y$, $z$ in feet, $t$ in hours, $u$ in degrees Fahrenheit, and $h^2$ in ft.$^2$ per hour. The thermal diffusivity (assumed constant in our work) can be defined by

$$h^2 = \frac{K}{\sigma \delta},$$

in terms of quantities of elementary physics,

$$K = \text{thermal conductivity,}$$
$$\sigma = \text{specific heat,}$$
$$\delta = \text{density,}$$

all pertaining to the material composing the solid whose temperature we seek.

Equation (1) is the equation which pertains in many types of diffusion, not just when heat is being diffused. It is often called the *equation of diffusion*.

The amount of heat which flows across an element of surface in a specified time is proportional to the rate of change of temperature in the direction normal (perpendicular) to that surface. Thus the flux of heat in the $x$ direction (across a surface normal to the $x$ direction) is taken to be

$$- K \frac{\partial u}{\partial x},$$

the constant of proportionality being $K$, the thermal conductivity of the material involved. The significance of the negative sign can be seen by considering an example in which the temperature increases with increasing $x$.

Then $\partial u/\partial x$ is positive but heat flows toward negative $x$, from the warmer portion to the colder portion; hence the flux is taken to be negative.

For us the expression for flux of heat will be used in forming boundary conditions involving insulation. If there is total insulation at a surface normal to the $x$ direction, then there is no flux of heat across that surface, so we put

$$\frac{\partial u}{\partial x} = 0$$

at that surface.

If the conditions in the problem are such that $u$ is independent of the coordinates $y$ and $z$, equation (1) becomes the one-dimensional equation of diffusion

(2) $$\frac{\partial u}{\partial t} = h^2 \frac{\partial^2 u}{\partial x^2} ,$$

which is also called the simple heat equation. Problems involving equation (2) will be solved in the following sections.

## 33. *Diffusion in a Semi-infinite Solid*

Consider the solid defined by $x \geqq 0$, occupying one half of three dimensional space. If the initial temperature within the solid and the conditions at the surface $x = 0$ are independent of the coordinates $y$ and $z$, the temperature $u$ will be independent of $y$ and $z$ for all $t > 0$. We may visualize, for example, a huge flat slab of concrete with an initial temperature distribution dependent upon only the distance from the plane surface of the slab. If the temperature at that surface is thereafter $(t > 0)$ maintained at some specified function of $t$, or if the surface is insulated, the problem of finding the temperature for all positive $x$ and $t$ is one involving the simple heat equation (2) of §32.

*Example.* Consider a semi-infinite slab $x \geqq 0$, initially at a fixed temperature $u = A$ and thereafter subjected to a surface temperature $(x \to 0^+)$ which is $u = B$ for $0 < t < t_0$ and then $u = 0$ for $t \geqq t_0$. Find the temperature within the solid for $x > 0$, $t > $ .

The boundary value problem to be solved is as follows:

(1) $$\frac{\partial u}{\partial t} = h^2 \frac{\partial^2 u}{\partial x^2} , \qquad \text{for } x > 0, \quad t > 0;$$

(2) $$t \to 0^+, \quad u \to A, \qquad \text{for } x > 0;$$

(3) $$x \to 0^+, \quad u \to B, \qquad \text{for } 0 < t < t_0,$$
$$u \to 0, \qquad \text{for } t > t_0;$$

(4) $$\text{Lim } u(x, t) \text{ exists, for each fixed } t > 0.$$
$$\scriptstyle x \to \infty$$

In this problem $A$, $B$ and $h^2$ are constants. We use the $\alpha$ function to reword the boundary condition (3) in the form

$$(5) \qquad x \to 0^+, \ u \to B[1 - \alpha(t - t_0)], \qquad \text{for } t > 0.$$

Note also that the physical problem dictates that the value of the limit in (4) is to be $A$. This furnishes us with an additional check on our work.

The problem satisfies the criteria, page 87, which suggest the use of the Laplace transform. Let

$$(6) \qquad L\{u(x, t)\} = w(x, s), \qquad x > 0, \ s > 0.$$

The equation (1) with the condition (2) is transformed into

$$sw - A = h^2 \frac{d^2 w}{dx^2}, \qquad x > 0,$$

or

$$(7) \qquad \frac{d^2 w}{dx^2} - \frac{s}{h^2} w = -\frac{A}{h^2}, \qquad x > 0.$$

The conditions (4) and (5) become

$$(8) \qquad \operatorname*{Lim}_{x \to \infty} w(x, s) \text{ exists, for fixed } s > 0,$$

$$(9) \qquad x \to 0^+, \ w \to \frac{B}{s}[1 - \exp(-t_0 s)].$$

The differential equation (7) has the general solution

$$(10) \quad w = c_1 \exp\left(-\frac{x\sqrt{s}}{h}\right) + c_2 \exp\left(\frac{x\sqrt{s}}{h}\right) + \frac{A}{s}, \qquad x > 0, \ s > 0,$$

in which $c_1$ and $c_2$ may be functions of $s$, but not of $x$. As $x \to \infty$, the $w$ of (10) will approach a limit if and only if $c_2 = 0$. Hence the condition (8) yields the result

$$(11) \qquad\qquad\qquad c_2 = 0$$

and the $w$ of (10) becomes

$$(12) \qquad\qquad w = c_1 \exp\left(-\frac{x\sqrt{s}}{h}\right) + \frac{A}{s}.$$

Using (9) we obtain, by letting $x \to 0^+$,

$$(13) \qquad\qquad \frac{B}{s}[1 - \exp(-t_0 s)] = c_1 + \frac{A}{s}.$$

Therefore the solution of the problem (7)–(9) is

$$(14) \quad w(x, s) = \frac{A}{s}\left[1 - \exp\left(-\frac{x\sqrt{s}}{h}\right)\right] + \frac{B}{s}\exp\left(-\frac{x\sqrt{s}}{h}\right)[1 - \exp(-t_0 s)].$$

We know that

(15) $$L^{-1}\left\{\frac{1}{s}\exp\left(-\frac{x\sqrt{s}}{h}\right)\right\} = \operatorname{erfc}\left(\frac{x}{2h\sqrt{t}}\right), \qquad x > 0.$$

Hence we may write

(16) $$L^{-1}\left\{\frac{1}{s}\exp\left(-\frac{x\sqrt{s}}{h}\right)\exp(-t_0 s)\right\} = \operatorname{erfc}\left(\frac{x}{2h|t-t_0|^{\frac{1}{2}}}\right)\alpha(t-t_0),$$

in which absolute value signs have been inserted to permit $t$ to be used in the range 0 to $t_0$ in which range the $\alpha$ function will force the right member of (16) to be zero.

We are now in a position to write the inverse transform of the $w$ of equation (14). For $x > 0$ and $t > 0$,

(17) $$u(x, t) = A\left[1 - \operatorname{erfc}\left(\frac{x}{2h\sqrt{t}}\right)\right] +$$

$$B\left[\operatorname{erfc}\left(\frac{x}{2h\sqrt{t}}\right) - \operatorname{erfc}\left(\frac{x}{2h|t-t_0|^{\frac{1}{2}}}\right)\alpha(t-t_0)\right],$$

or

(18) $$u(x, t) = A\operatorname{erf}\left(\frac{x}{2h\sqrt{t}}\right) +$$

$$B\left[\operatorname{erfc}\left(\frac{x}{2h\sqrt{t}}\right) - \operatorname{erfc}\left(\frac{x}{2h|t-t_0|^{\frac{1}{2}}}\right)\alpha(t-t_0)\right].$$

The $u$ of (17), or of (18), is the desired solution.

It is a matter of direct substitution to show that each term of (18) is a solution of the one-dimensional heat equation. That the conditions (2), (3) and (4) are also satisfied follows rapidly from the properties

$$\lim_{z\to 0}\operatorname{erf} z = 0, \qquad \lim_{z\to\infty}\operatorname{erf} z = 1$$

and the corresponding properties of the erfc function. Indeed, for the $u$ of (18),

As $x \to 0^+$, $u \to A\cdot 0 + B[1 - \alpha(t-t_0)] = B[1 - \alpha(t-t_0)]$, for $t > 0$;
As $t \to 0^+$, $u \to A\cdot 1 + B(0-0) = A$, for $x > 0$;
As $x \to \infty$, $u \to A\cdot 1 + B\cdot 0 = A$, for $0 < t < t_0$,
As $x \to \infty$, $u \to A\cdot 1 + B(0-0) = A$, for $t > t_0$.

## 34. Diffusion in a Slab of Finite Width

Consider a huge flat slab of concrete, or some other material reasonably near homogeneity in texture. Let the thickness of the slab be $c$ units of length. Let the coordinate $x$ denote distance from one face of the slab and assume that the slab extends very far in the $y$ and $z$ directions. Assume that the initial temperature of the slab is a constant $A$ and that the surfaces $x = 0$, $x = c$ are maintained at zero temperature for all $t > 0$. If the slab is considered infinite in the $y$ and $z$ directions, or more specifically, if we treat only cross sections nearby (far from the distant surfaces of the slab), then the temperature $u$ at any time $t$ and position $x$ is determined by the boundary value problem:

$$(1) \qquad \frac{\partial u}{\partial t} = h^2 \frac{\partial^2 u}{\partial x^2}, \qquad \text{for } t > 0, \quad 0 < x < c;$$

$$(2) \qquad t \to 0^+, \quad u \to A, \qquad \text{for } 0 < x < c;$$

$$(3) \qquad x \to 0^+, \quad u \to 0, \qquad \text{for } t > 0;$$

$$(4) \qquad x \to c^-, \quad u \to 0, \qquad \text{for } t > 0.$$

We shall solve the corresponding problem in canonical variables. That is, in (1)–(4) we replace

$$(5) \qquad x \text{ by } cx, \ t \text{ by } \frac{c^2 t}{h^2}, \ u \text{ by } Au.$$

In the new $x$, $t$ and $u$ the problem to be solved is

$$(6) \qquad \frac{\partial u}{\partial t} = \frac{\partial^2 u}{\partial x^2}, \qquad \text{for } t > 0, \quad 0 < x < 1:$$

$$(7) \qquad t \to 0^+, \quad u \to 1, \qquad \text{for } 0 < x < 1;$$

$$(8) \qquad x \to 0^+, \quad u \to 0, \qquad \text{for } t > 0;$$

$$(9) \qquad x \to 1^-, \quad u \to 0, \qquad \text{for } t > 0.$$

Let

$$(10) \qquad L\{u(x, t)\} = w(x, s).$$

Application of the Laplace operator transforms the problem (6)–(9) into

$$(11) \qquad sw - 1 = \frac{d^2 w}{dx^2}, \qquad \text{for } 0 < x < 1;$$

$$(12) \qquad x \to 0^+, \ w \to 0;$$

$$(13) \qquad x \to 1^-, \ w \to 0.$$

The general solution of (11) may be written

$$(14) \qquad w = c_1 \sinh(x\sqrt{s}) + c_2 \cosh(x\sqrt{s}) + \frac{1}{s}.$$

From (12) it follows that

$$(15) \qquad 0 = c_2 + \frac{1}{s}$$

and (13) yields

$$(16) \qquad 0 = c_1 \sinh \sqrt{s} + c_2 \cosh \sqrt{s} + \frac{1}{s}.$$

By solving (15) and (16) we obtain

$$(17) \qquad c_2 = -\frac{1}{s}, \; c_1 = \frac{\cosh \sqrt{s} - 1}{s \sinh \sqrt{s}},$$

from which we see that

$$(18) \qquad w = \frac{1}{s} + \frac{(\cosh \sqrt{s} - 1) \sinh(x \sqrt{s}) - \sinh \sqrt{s} \cosh(x \sqrt{s})}{s \sinh \sqrt{s}}.$$

Since

$$\sinh B_1 \cosh B_2 - \cosh B_1 \sinh B_2 = \sinh (B_1 - B_2),$$

the $w$ of (18) may be written in the form

$$(19) \qquad w(x, s) = \frac{1}{s} \left[ 1 - \frac{\sinh(x \sqrt{s})}{\sinh \sqrt{s}} - \frac{\sinh\{(1 - x)\sqrt{s}\}}{\sinh \sqrt{s}} \right].$$

The desired solution $u(x, t)$ is the inverse of the $w(x, s)$ of (19) with $x$ on the range $0 < x < 1$.

We already know from equation (29) page 81, that for $0 < x < 1$,

$$(20) \quad L^{-1} \left\{ \frac{\sinh(x \sqrt{s})}{s \sinh \sqrt{s}} \right\} = \sum_{n=0}^{\infty} \left[ \mathrm{erfc} \left( \frac{1 - x + 2n}{2\sqrt{t}} \right) - \mathrm{erfc} \left( \frac{1 + x + 2n}{2\sqrt{t}} \right) \right].$$

Applying (20) twice, once with $x$ and once with $(1 - x)$ replacing $x$, we obtain from (19) the desired solution

$$(21) \quad u(x, t) = 1 - \sum_{n=0}^{\infty} \left[ \mathrm{erfc} \left( \frac{1 - x + 2n}{2\sqrt{t}} \right) - \mathrm{erfc} \left( \frac{1 + x + 2n}{2\sqrt{t}} \right) \right]$$

$$- \sum_{n=0}^{\infty} \left[ \mathrm{erfc} \left( \frac{x + 2n}{2\sqrt{t}} \right) - \mathrm{erfc} \left( \frac{2 - x + 2n}{2\sqrt{t}} \right) \right].$$

The complementary error functions in (21) may be replaced by error functions, since

$$(22) \qquad \mathrm{erfc} \, z = 1 - \mathrm{erf} \, z.$$

With the aid of the properties

$$(23) \qquad \mathrm{erfc} \, 0 = 1, \quad \underset{z \to \infty}{\mathrm{Lim}} \, \mathrm{erfc} \, z = 0,$$

the solution (21) is easily verified, assuming that the summation sign and the pertinent limits may be interchanged. With the theorems of advanced calculus the assumption can be shown to be valid.

From (21) we get, as $x \to 0^+$,

$$u \to 1 - \sum_{n=0}^{\infty} \left[ \operatorname{erfc} \left( \frac{2n+1}{2\sqrt{t}} \right) - \operatorname{erfc} \left( \frac{2n+1}{2\sqrt{t}} \right) \right]$$

$$- \sum_{n=0}^{\infty} \left[ \operatorname{erfc} \left( \frac{n}{\sqrt{t}} \right) - \operatorname{erfc} \left( \frac{n+1}{\sqrt{t}} \right) \right].$$

In the first series each term is zero. The second series telescopes; in it replace the series by the limit of the partial sums to get

$$u \to 1 - \operatorname*{Lim}_{n \to \infty} \sum_{k=0}^{n} \left[ \operatorname{erfc} \left( \frac{k}{\sqrt{t}} \right) - \operatorname{erfc} \left( \frac{k+1}{\sqrt{t}} \right) \right],$$

or

$$u \to 1 - \operatorname*{Lim}_{n \to \infty} \left[ \operatorname{erfc} 0 - \operatorname{erfc} \left( \frac{n+1}{\sqrt{t}} \right) \right].$$

For fixed $t > 0$, $(n+1)/\sqrt{t} \to \infty$ as $n \to \infty$. Hence by (23),

(24) $$u \to 1 - 1 + 0 = 0, \qquad \text{as } x \to 0^+.$$

The solution (21) is unchanged when $x$ is replaced by $(1 - x)$, because the two series merely change places. Therefore, because of (24),

(25) $$u \to 0, \qquad \text{as } x \to 1^-.$$

For any $x$ in the range $0 < x < 1$, the argument of each erfc in (21) is positive and approaches infinity as $t \to 0^+$. Hence each erfc $\to 1$ and each term of the two series $\to 0$. Thus, because the order of limit and summation can be interchanged,

(26) $$u \to 1, \qquad \text{as } t \to 0^+, \qquad \text{for } 0 < x < 1.$$

Perhaps the most valuable single fact about the solution (21) is the fact that the series converge very rapidly for small $t$ because the arguments of the various erfc functions are then very large. By the methods of separation of variables and Fourier series the problem (6)–(9) at the start of this section can be shown to have the solution

(27) $$u(x, t) = \frac{4}{\pi} \sum_{k=0}^{\infty} \frac{\exp[-\pi^2(2k+1)^2 t]\sin[(2k+1)\pi x]}{2k+1}.$$

The solutions given by (21) and (27) are identical, though the uniqueness of such solutions is not proved here.

The series in (27) converges rapidly for large $t$ and slowly for small $t$. The series in (21) converge rapidly for small $t$ and slowly for large $t$. The two forms of solution complement each other neatly.

**EXERCISE**

1. Interpret and solve the following problem:

$$\frac{\partial u}{\partial t} = \frac{\partial^2 u}{\partial x^2}, \qquad \text{for } t > 0,\ 0 < x < 1;$$

$$t \to 0^+,\ u \to 1, \qquad \text{for } 0 < x < 1;$$

$$x \to 0^+,\ u \to 0, \qquad \text{for } t > 0;$$

$$x \to 1^-,\ \frac{\partial u}{\partial x} \to 0, \qquad \text{for } t > 0.$$

*Ans.* $u = 1 - \sum\limits_{n=0}^{\infty} (-1)^n \left[ \operatorname{erfc}\left(\dfrac{2n + x}{2\sqrt{t}}\right) + \operatorname{erfc}\left(\dfrac{2n + 2 - x}{2\sqrt{t}}\right) \right].$

# Table of Transforms

Whenever $n$ is used, it denotes a non-negative integer.

The range of validity may be determined from the appropriate text material. Many other transforms will be found in the examples and exercises.

| $f(s) = L\{F(t)\}$ | $F(t)$ |
|---|---|
| $f(s - a)$ | $e^{at}F(t)$ |
| $f(as)$ | $\dfrac{1}{a} F\left(\dfrac{t}{a}\right)$ |
| $f(as + b)$ | $\dfrac{1}{a} \exp\left(-\dfrac{bt}{a}\right) F\left(\dfrac{t}{a}\right)$ |
| $\dfrac{1}{s} e^{-cs}, \quad c > 0$ | $\alpha(t - c) = 0, \quad 0 \le t < c,$<br>$= 1, t \ge c$ |
| $e^{-cs}f(s), \quad c > 0$ | $F(t - c)\alpha(t - c)$ |
| $f_1(s)\, f_2(s)$ | $\displaystyle\int_0^t F_1(\beta)\, F_2(t - \beta)\, d\beta$ |
| $\dfrac{1}{s}$ | $1$ |
| $\dfrac{1}{s^{n+1}}$ | $\dfrac{t^n}{n!}$ |
| $\dfrac{1}{s^{x+1}}, \quad x > -1$ | $\dfrac{t^x}{\Gamma(x + 1)}$ |
| $s^{-\frac{1}{2}}$ | $(\pi t)^{-\frac{1}{2}}$ |
| $\dfrac{1}{s + a}$ | $e^{-at}$ |

| $f(s) = L\{F(t)\}$ | $F(t)$ |
|---|---|
| $\dfrac{1}{(s+a)^{n+1}}$ | $\dfrac{t^n e^{-at}}{n!}$ |
| $\dfrac{k}{s^2 + k^2}$ | $\sin kt$ |
| $\dfrac{s}{s^2 + k^2}$ | $\cos kt$ |
| $\dfrac{k}{s^2 - k^2}$ | $\sinh kt$ |
| $\dfrac{s}{s^2 - k^2}$ | $\cosh kt$ |
| $\dfrac{2k^3}{(s^2 + k^2)^2}$ | $\sin kt - kt \cos kt$ |
| $\dfrac{2ks}{(s^2 + k^2)^2}$ | $t \sin kt$ |
| $\dfrac{1}{s}\exp(-c\sqrt{s}), \quad c > 0$ | $\operatorname{erfc}\left(\dfrac{c}{2\sqrt{t}}\right)$ |
| $\dfrac{1}{s\sqrt{s+1}}$ | $\operatorname{erf}\left(\sqrt{t}\right)$ |
| $\ln\left(1 + \dfrac{1}{s}\right)$ | $\dfrac{1 - e^{-t}}{t}$ |
| $\ln\dfrac{s+k}{s-k}$ | $\dfrac{2\sinh kt}{t}$ |

| $f(s) = L\{F(t)\}$ | $F(t)$ |
|---|---|
| $\ln\left(1 - \dfrac{k^2}{s^2}\right)$ | $\dfrac{2}{t}\,(1 - \cosh kt)$ |
| $\ln\left(1 + \dfrac{k^2}{s^2}\right)$ | $\dfrac{2}{t}\,(1 - \cos kt)$ |
| $\text{Arctan}\,\dfrac{k}{s}$ | $\dfrac{\sin kt}{t}$ |
| $\dfrac{1}{s}\exp\left(-\dfrac{x}{s}\right)$ | $J_0\,(2\sqrt{xt}\,)$ |
| $\dfrac{1}{s^{n+1}}\exp\left(-\dfrac{x}{s}\right)$ | $\left(\dfrac{t}{x}\right)^{\frac{1}{2}n} J_n(2\sqrt{xt}\,)$ |
| $\dfrac{1}{\sqrt{s^2 + x^2}}$ | $J_0(xt)$ |
| $1 - \dfrac{s}{\sqrt{s^2 + x^2}}$ | $xJ_1(xt)$ |

# Index

**105**